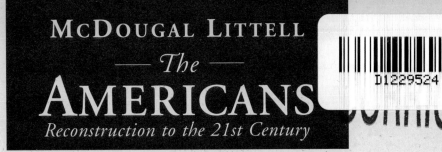

McDOUGAL LITTELL
— The —
AMERICANS
Reconstruction to the 21st Century

In-Depth Resources: Unit 6

Living with Great Turmoil

Weeks-Townsend Memorial Library
Union College
Barbourville, KY 40906

McDougal Littell
A HOUGHTON MIFFLIN COMPANY
Evanston, Illinois • Boston • Dallas

Acknowledgments

CHAPTER 20

Excerpt from *Unsafe at Any Speed* by Ralph Nader. Copyright © 1965 by Ralph Nader. Reprinted by permission of the author.

Excerpt from *Paper Wings* by Marly Swick. Copyright © 1996 by Marly Swick. Reprinted by permission of HarperCollins Publishers, Inc.

CHAPTER 21

Excerpt from "I Have a Dream" by Martin Luther King, Jr. Copyright © 1963 by Martin Luther King, Jr., renewed 1991 by Coretta Scott King. Reprinted by arrangement with The Heirs to the Estate of Martin Luther King, Jr., c/o Writers House, Inc. as agent for the proprietor.

Excerpt from *And All Our Wounds Forgiven* by Julius Lester. Copyright © 1994 by Julius Lester. Published by Arcade Publishing, New York, New York. Reprinted by permission of the publisher.

CHAPTER 22

Excerpt from *Dear America: Letters Home from Vietnam,* edited by Bernard Edelman for The New York Vietnam Veterans Memorial Commission. Published by W. W. Norton and Company, 1985. Reprinted by permission of Bernard Edelman.

Excerpt from *They Should Have Served That Cup of Coffee,* edited by Dick Cluster. Reprinted with permission from the publisher, South End Press, 116 Saint Botolph Street, Boston, MA 02115.

Excerpt from *In Country* by Bobbie Ann Mason. Copyright © 1985 by Bobbie Ann Mason. Reprinted by permission of HarperCollins Publishers, Inc.

CHAPTER 23

Excerpt from *César Chávez: Autobiography of La Causa* by Jacques E. Levy, published by W. W. Norton & Company, 1975. Used by permission of the author.

Excerpt from *The Feminine Mystique* by Betty Friedan. Copyright © 1983, 1974, 1973, 1963 by Betty Friedan. Reprinted by permission of W. W. Norton & Company, Inc.

"Woodstock" by Joni Mitchell. Copyright © 1969, 1974 by Siquomb Publishing Corp. All rights reserved. Used by permission of Warner Bros. Publications, Inc.

Excerpt from "Los Vendidos" by Luis Valdez, from *Luis Valdez, Early Works: Actos, Bernabé and Pensamiento Serpentino* (Houston: Arte Público Press, University of Houston, 1971). Reprinted with permission from the publisher, Arte Público Press.

Copyright © by McDougal Littell, a division of Houghton Mifflin Company.
All rights reserved.

Permission is hereby granted to teachers to reprint or photocopy in classroom quantities the pages or sheets in this work that carry a McDougal Littell copyright notice. These pages are designed to be reproduced by teachers for use in their classes with accompanying McDougal Littell material, provided each copy made shows the copyright notice. Such copies may not be sold, and further distribution is expressly prohibited. Except as authorized above, prior written permission must be obtained from McDougal Littell, a division of Houghton Mifflin Company, to reproduce or transmit this work or portions thereof in any other form or by any other electronic or mechanical means, including any information storage or retrieval system, unless expressly permitted by federal copyright law. Address inquiries to Supervisor, Rights and Permissions, McDougal Littell, a division of Houghton Mifflin Company, P.O. Box 1667, Evanston, Illinois 60204.

Printed in the United States of America.

ISBN-13: 978-0-618-17611-3   ISBN-10: 0-618-17611-X

9 10 11 12 – MDO – 08 07 06

Unit 6 Living with Great Turmoil 1954–1975

CHAPTER 20 The New Frontier and the Great Society, 1960–1968

CHAPTER 21 Civil Rights, 1954–1970

CHAPTER 22 The Vietnam War Years, 1954–1975

CHAPTER 23 An Era of Social Change, 1960–1975

Name _____ Date _____

CHAPTER 20

Section 1

GUIDED READING *Kennedy and the Cold War*

A. As you read this section, complete the time line by taking notes about the election of John F. Kennedy and about his handling of several Soviet-American confrontations.

1957	Launch of *Sputnik 1*	1. What were some of the factors that helped John F. Kennedy win the presidency?
1960	U-2 incident Alignment of Cuba with the Soviet Union U.S. presidential election →	
1961	Bay of Pigs →	2. What were the results of the Bay of Pigs invasion?
	Berlin crisis →	3. How was the Berlin crisis resolved?
1962	Cuban missile crisis →	4. What were the effects of the Cuban missile crisis?
1963	Installation of hot line →	5. Why was the hot line installed?
	Negotiation of Limited Test Ban Treaty →	6. What would the Limited Test Ban Treaty eventually do?

B. On the back of this paper, briefly explain Kennedy's policy of **flexible response.**

Name _____ Date _____

A. As you read this section, take notes to answer questions about President Kennedy's attempts to solve domestic and international problems.

The New Frontier: Fulfilled Promises

Problems	What did Kennedy believe the government could do to solve the problem?	What programs, laws, and accomplishments resulted from Kennedy's beliefs?
1. Economic recession		
2. Poverty abroad		
3. Soviet successes in space		

The New Frontier: Unfulfilled Promises

Rejected Proposals	Later Proposals
4. What reform proposals did Kennedy make that were rejected by a conservative Congress?	5. In 1963, what proposals did Kennedy make but never had the chance to guide through Congress?

B. On the back of this paper, define **mandate.** Then explain what the **Warren Commission** was and what it did.

Name _____ Date _____

CHAPTER
20
Section 3

GUIDED READING *The Great Society*

A. As you read, note what each program or law did or was intended to do.

Program or Law	Objectives or Results
1. Tax-cut bill of 1964	
2. Civil Rights Act of 1964	
3. Economic Opportunity Act of 1964	
4. Elementary and Secondary Education Act	
5. Medicare	
6. Medicaid	
7. Immigration Act of 1965	

B. Note how the Court ruled in each case or what the decision accomplished.

Court Cases	Results
1. *Brown* v. *Board of Education*	
2. *Baker* v. *Carr*	
3. *Mapp* v. *Ohio*	
4. *Gideon* v. *Wainright*	
5. *Escobedo* v. *Illinois*	
6. *Miranda* v. *Arizona*	

Name _____ Date _____

BUILDING VOCABULARY *The New Frontier and the Great Society*

A. Matching Match the description in the second column with the term or name in the first column. Write the appropriate letter next to the word.

_____ 1. reapportionment   a. provided help to Latin America

_____ 2. Fidel Castro   b. barrier between East and West Berlin

_____ 3. Alliance for Progress   c. redrawing of election districts

_____ 4. Lyndon Baines Johnson   d. leader of Cuba

_____ 5. flexible response   e. succeeded Kennedy as president

_____ 6. Berlin Wall   f. reliance on conventional rather than nuclear warfare

B. Multiple Choice Circle the letter before the term or name that best completes the sentence.

1. Lyndon Johnson's domestic programs were known collectively as the (a) New Frontier (b) Great Society (c) Fair Deal.

2. The program that extended health insurance to welfare recipients was (a) Medicare (b) Medicaid (c) Social Security.

3. The body that performed the official investigation into the assassination of President Kennedy was the (a) Warren Commission (b) Peace Corps (c) Tennessee Valley Authority.

4. All of the following were programs of the Economic Opportunity Act except (a) VISTA (c) Project Head Start (c) Medicare.

5. The Immigration Act of 1965 sought to end a long-standing policy that favored immigrants from (a) Europe (b) Africa (c) Asia.

C. Writing Use the following related terms together in a paragraph.

    hot line   **Limited Test Ban Treaty**

CHAPTER 20

Section 1

SKILLBUILDER PRACTICE *Predicting Effects*

When Richard Nixon and John F. Kennedy faced each other in history's first televised debate, the world of politics changed forever. As journalist Russell Baker wrote at the time, "That night, image replaced the printed word as the natural language of politics." Use the table and questions on this page to predict the impact of television on campaigns of the future. (See Skillbuilder Handbook, p. R20.)

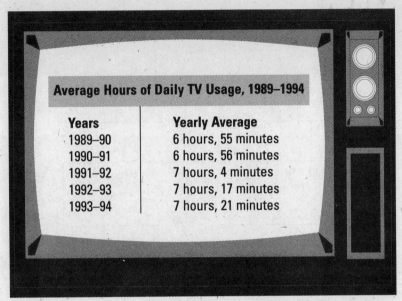

Average Hours of Daily TV Usage, 1989–1994	
Years	**Yearly Average**
1989–90	6 hours, 55 minutes
1990–91	6 hours, 56 minutes
1991–92	7 hours, 4 minutes
1992–93	7 hours, 17 minutes
1993–94	7 hours, 21 minutes

Source: *1996 Information Please Almanac*

1. A trend is a general pattern of change over time. What overall trend characterized television viewing time during the early 1990s?

_____

2. Based on this trend, what predictions would you make about television viewing time in the late 1990s?

_____

3. Suppose you were a political candidate. How might predictions about television viewing time influence your decisions about campaign spending?

_____

_____

Name _____ Date _____

Sequencing

A. Identify key events of the Cold War associated with each date and explain their significance.

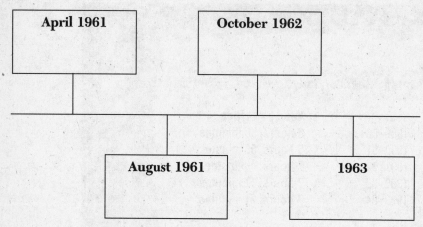

Completion

B. Select the term or name that best completes the sentence.

Robert Kennedy	Bessie Smith	Robert McNamara
Dean Rusk	Richard Nixon	Rough Riders
Green Berets	defense spending	Dwight Eisenhower

1. John Kennedy defeated _____ to become president in 1960.

2. Kennedy appointed _____ as the nation's attorney general.

3. As president, Kennedy increased _____ in order to build up the nation's conventional forces.

4. As part of this flexible response strategy, Kennedy created an elite branch of the army, known popularly as the _____ .

Name _____   Date _____

CHAPTER
20
Section 2

RETEACHING ACTIVITY *The New Frontier*

Finding Main Ideas

The following questions deal with events during President Kennedy's term in office.
Answer them in the space provided.

1. How did the Kennedy administration battle the recession? What were some examples of
   this strategy?

   _____

   _____

2. What was the difference between the Peace Corps and the Alliance for Progress?

   _____

   _____

3. What impact did the growth of the nation's space program have on American society?

   _____

   _____

4. What difficulties did Kennedy face in his dealings with Congress? Why didn't he act more
   forcefully to push through his measures?

   _____

   _____

5. For what reason did President Kennedy travel to Dallas, Texas, on November 22, 1963?

   _____

   _____

6. What did the Warren Commission determine about the assassination of President
   Kennedy?

   _____

   _____

CHAPTER
20
Section 3

RETEACHING ACTIVITY *The Great Society*

Completion

Choose the best answer for each item. Write the letter of your answer in the blank.

_____ 1. President Kennedy asked Lyndon Johnson to be his running mate in 1960 in part to help him win key states in the
a. West.
b. Midwest.
c. Northeast.
d. South.

_____ 2. In the presidential election of 1964, Lyndon Johnson won a landslide victory over
a. Barry Goldwater.
b. Richard Nixon.
c. Robert Weaver.
d. Earl Warren.

_____ 3. The Supreme Court case ordering that all suspects must be read their rights before questioning was
a. *Escobedo* v. *Illinois.*
b. *Miranda* v. *Arizona.*
c. *Reynolds* v. *Sims.*
d. *Brown* v. *Board of Education of Topeka.*

_____ 4. The Great Society program that played a key role in the "war on poverty" was the
a. Civil Rights Act.
b. Economic Opportunity Act.
c. Immigration Act of 1965.
d. Wilderness Preservation Act.

_____ 5. Medicare provided greater health benefits for
a. the poor.
b. children.
c. the elderly.
d. single mothers.

_____ 6. *Unsafe at Any Speed* was a best-selling book that alleged a widespread neglect for safety in the
a. automobile industry.
b. airline industry.
c. railroad industry.
d. meatpacking industry.

Name _____   Date _____

CHAPTER

20

Section 1

GEOGRAPHY APPLICATION: PLACE

Divided Germany and the Berlin Wall

Directions: Read the paragraphs below and study the maps carefully. Then answer the questions that follow.

After winning World War II, the Allies divided Germany into four separately administered zones. The Soviet Union controlled the eastern part of the country, while the United States, Great Britain, and France controlled the western part, which was soon united into one political division.

The same divisions existed within the former German capital of Berlin, and the city became a frequent source of U.S.-Soviet tension in the postwar era. Between 1949 and 1961, about 2.7 million East Germans fled to freedom in West Germany. Hundreds of thousands of them escaped simply by making their way into relatively open West Berlin and then flying to West Germany. In the summer of 1961, about 1,500 East Germans a day were fleeing into West Berlin. As a result, a wall 13 feet high and about 100 miles long was built around West Berlin that fall. The Hungarian composer György Ligeti described the walled-in region as "a surrealist cage in which those inside are free."

The Berlin Wall created an emotional crisis for the city's residents. The wall cut across 62 city streets and 131 outlying roads. Relatives and friends were separated. Those living in East Berlin and working in West Berlin lost their jobs. During the wall's 28 years of existence, about 80 people were killed trying to climb over it and get inside.

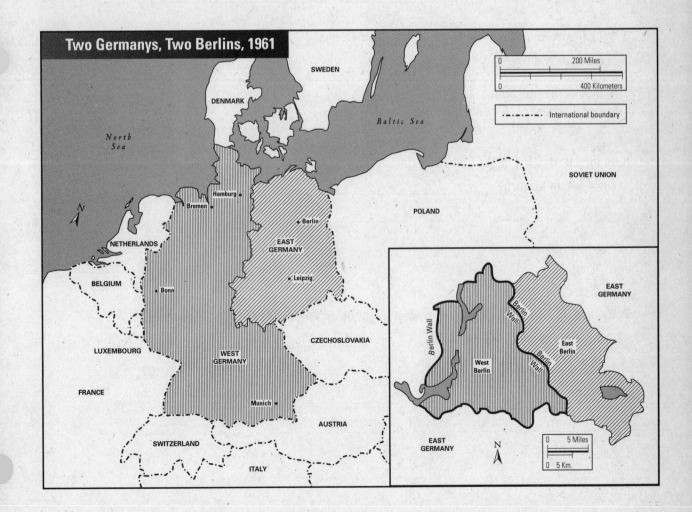

Interpreting Text and Visuals

1. Which part of Germany was controlled by the United States, Great Britain, and France after World War II? _____

2. Who controlled the larger part of postwar Germany—the Soviet Union or the three Western powers? _____

3. In which part of Germany was Berlin located? _____

4. Use a ruler and the scale on the main map to determine approximately how far Berlin lay from the closest point in West Germany. _____

   In what way do you think Berlin's location was a problem for the Western powers?

   _____
   _____
   _____

5. Which government—West Germany's or East Germany's—do you think erected the Berlin Wall? _____

   Why was the wall built? _____

   _____

6. Before 1961, what might have been the best way for someone living in Leipzig to escape to Munich? _____

   _____
   _____

7. Explain the irony—the opposite of what might be expected—in György Ligeti's characterization of West Berlin. _____

   _____
   _____
   _____

CHAPTER 20

Section 1

PRIMARY SOURCE # John F. Kennedy's Inaugural Address

On January 20, 1961, John F. Kennedy was sworn in as the 35th president of the United States. As you read Kennedy's inaugural address, think about the challenge that he issues to his fellow Americans.

We observe today not a victory of party but a celebration of freedom—symbolizing an end as well as a beginning—signifying renewal as well as change. For I have sworn before you and Almighty God the same solemn oath our forebears prescribed nearly a century and three-quarters ago.

The world is very different now. For man holds in his mortal hands the power to abolish all forms of human poverty and all forms of human life. And yet the same revolutionary beliefs for which our forebears fought are still at issue around the globe—the belief that the rights of man come not from the generosity of the state but from the hand of God.

We dare not forget today that we are the heirs of that first revolution. Let the word go forth from this time and place, to friend and foe alike, that the torch has been passed to a new generation of Americans—born in this century, tempered by war, disciplined by a hard and bitter peace, proud of our ancient heritage—and unwilling to witness or permit the slow undoing of those human rights to which this nation has always been committed and to which we are committed today at home and around the world.

Let every nation know, whether it wishes us well or ill, that we shall pay any price, bear any burden, meet any hardship, support any friend, oppose any foe to assure the survival and the success of liberty.

This much we pledge—and more.

To those old allies whose cultural and spiritual origins we share, we pledge the loyalty of faithful friends. United, there is little we cannot do in a host of cooperative ventures. Divided, there is little we can do—for we dare not meet a powerful challenge at odds and split asunder.

To those new states whom we welcome to the ranks of the free, we pledge our word that one form of colonial control shall not have passed away merely to be replaced by a far more iron tyranny. We shall not always expect to find them supporting our view. But we shall always hope to find them strongly supporting their own freedom—and to remember that, in the past, those who foolishly sought power by riding the back of the tiger ended up inside.

To those people in the huts and villages of half the globe struggling to break the bonds of mass misery, we pledge our best efforts to help them help themselves, for whatever period is required—not because the Communists may be doing it, not because we seek their votes, but because it is right. If a free society cannot help the many who are poor, it cannot save the few who are rich.

To our sister republics south of our border, we offer a special pledge—to convert our good words into good deeds—in a new alliance for progress—to assist free men and free governments in casting off the chains of poverty. But this peaceful revolution of hope cannot become the prey of hostile powers. Let all our neighbors know that we shall join with them to oppose aggression or subversion anywhere in the Americas. And let every other power know that this hemisphere intends to remain the master of its own house.

To that world assembly of sovereign states, the United Nations, our last best hope in an age where the instruments of war have far outpaced the instruments of peace, we renew our pledge of support—to prevent it from becoming merely a forum for invective—to strengthen its shield of the new and the weak—and to enlarge the area in which its writ may run.

Finally, to those nations who would make themselves our adversary, we offer not a pledge but a request—that both sides begin anew the quest for peace before the dark powers of destruction unleashed by science engulf all humanity in planned or accidental self-destruction. We dare not tempt them with weakness. For only when our arms are sufficient beyond doubt can we be certain beyond doubt that they will never be employed.

But neither can two great and powerful groups of nations take comfort from our present course—

both sides overburdened by the cost of modern weapons, both rightly alarmed by the steady spread of the deadly atom, yet both racing to alter that uncertain balance of terror that stays the hand of mankind's final war.

So let us begin anew—remembering on both sides that civility is not a sign of weakness, and sincerity is always subject to proof. Let us never negotiate out of fear. But let us never fear to negotiate.

Let both sides explore what problems unite us instead of belaboring those problems which divide us.

Let both sides, for the first time, formulate serious and precise proposals for the inspection and control of arms—and bring the absolute power to destroy other nations under the absolute control of all nations.

Let both sides seek to invoke the wonders of science instead of its terrors. Together let us explore the stars, conquer the deserts, eradicate disease, tap the ocean depths, and encourage the arts and commerce.

Let both sides unite to heed in all corners of the earth the command of Isaiah—to "undo the heavy burdens . . . [and] let the oppressed go free."

And if a beachhead of cooperation may push back the jungle of suspicion, let both sides join in creating a new endeavor, not a new balance of power but a new world of law, where the strong are just and the weak secure and the peace preserved.

All this will not be finished in the first 100 days. Nor will it be finished in the first 1,000 days, nor in the life of this administration, nor even perhaps in our lifetime on this planet. But let us begin.

In your hands, my fellow citizens, more than mine, will rest the final success or failure of our course. Since this country was founded, each generation of Americans has been summoned to give testimony to its national loyalty. The graves of young Americans who answered the call to service surround the globe.

Now the trumpet summons us again—not as a call to bear arms, though arms we need—not as a call to battle, though embattled we are—but a call to bear the burden of a long twilight struggle, year in and year out, "rejoicing in hope, patient in tribulation"—a struggle against the common enemies of man: tyranny, poverty, disease, and war itself.

Can we forge against these enemies a grand and global alliance, North and South, East and West, that can assure a more fruitful life for all mankind? Will you join in that historic effort?

In the long history of the world, only a few generations have been granted the role of defending freedom in its hour of maximum danger. I do not shrink from this responsibility—I welcome it. I do not believe that any of us would exchange places with any other people or any other generation. The energy, the faith, the devotion which we bring to this endeavor will light our country and all who serve it—and the glow from that fire can truly light the world.

And so, my fellow Americans—ask not what your country can do for you—ask what you can do for your country.

My fellow citizens of the world—ask not what America will do for you but what together we can do for the freedom of man.

Finally, whether you are citizens of America or citizens of the world, ask of us here the same high standards of strength and sacrifice which we ask of you. With a good conscience our only sure reward, with history the final judge of our deeds, let us go forth to lead the land we love, asking His blessing and His help, but knowing that here on earth God's work must truly be our own.

from *Department of State Bulletin,* February 6, 1961.

Activity Options

1. Kennedy inspired the nation with his youth, his charisma, and his energy. With a small group of classmates, select several passages from this speech that you think Americans found particularly inspiring or meaningful at the time. Then read these passages aloud to the rest of the class.
2. President Kennedy challenged Americans to ask themselves what they can do for their country. Ask yourself the same question—what can you do to make your country stronger, safer, and more just? With a group of classmates, brainstorm ideas and draw up a plan for putting one idea into action.

Name _____ Date _____

PRIMARY SOURCE Political Cartoon

*Herbert Block drew this political cartoon shortly after the Cuban missile crisis,
the most serious U.S.-Soviet confrontation. Notice that, unlike many American
politicians and journalists who were severely critical of the Soviet leader at the
time, Block depicts Nikita Khrushchev as an equal of President Kennedy in struggling to contain nuclear war.*

"LET'S GET A LOCK FOR THIS THING"

"Let's get a lock for this thing" from *Herblock: A Cartoonist's Life* (Macmillan, 1993).

Discussion Questions

1. What message does this cartoon send to the
   leaders of the United States and the Soviet
   Union?

2. Considering the climate of the Cold War in
   1962, do you think the spirit of this cartoon is
   overly optimistic? Why or why not?

CHAPTER
20
Section 3

PRIMARY SOURCE *from* Unsafe at Any Speed

In 1964 the assistant secretary of labor hired lawyer and consumer advocate Ralph Nader as a consultant on automobile safety. Nader's government report, which was later published in book form, blasted the automobile industry. According to this excerpt from Nader's book, why did car manufacturers resist making safer vehicles?

For over half a century the automobile has brought death, injury, and the most inestimable sorrow and deprivation to millions of people. With Medea-like intensity, this mass trauma began rising sharply four years ago, reflecting new and unexpected ravages by the motor vehicle. A 1959 Department of Commerce report projected that 51,000 persons would be killed by automobiles in 1975. That figure will probably be reached in 1965, a decade ahead of schedule.

A transportation specialist, Wilfred Owen, wrote in 1946, "There is little question that the public will not tolerate for long an annual traffic toll of 40,000 to 50,000 fatalities." Time has shown Owen to be wrong. Unlike aviation, marine, or rail transportation, the highway-transport system can inflict tremendous casualties and property damage without in the least affecting the visibility of the system. Plane crashes, for example, jeopardize the attraction of flying for potential passengers and therefore strike at the heart of the air-transport economy. They motivate preventative efforts. The situation is different on the roads.

Highway accidents were estimated to have cost this country, in 1964, $8.3 billion in property damage, medical expenses, lost wages, and insurance overhead expenses. Add an equivalent sum to comprise roughly the indirect costs and the total amounts to over 2 percent of the gross national product. But these are not the kind of costs which fall on the builders of motor vehicles (excepting a few successful law suits for negligent construction of the vehicle) and thus do not pinch the proper foot. Instead, the costs fall to users of vehicles, who are in no position to dictate safer automobile designs.

In fact, the gigantic costs of the highway carnage in this country support a service industry. A vast array of services—medical, police, administrative, legal, insurance, automotive repair, and funeral—stand equipped to handle the direct and indirect consequences of accident-injuries. Traffic accidents create economic demands for these services running into billions of dollars. It is in the post-accident response that lawyers and physicians and other specialists

labor. This is where the remuneration lies and this is where the talent and energies go. Working in the area of prevention of these casualties earns few fees. Consequently our society has an intricate organization to handle direct and indirect aftermaths of collisions. But the true mark of a humane society must be what it does about *prevention* of accident injuries, not the cleaning up of them afterward.

Unfortunately, there is little in the dynamics of the automobile accident industry that works for its reduction. Doctors, lawyers, engineers, and other specialists have failed in their primary professional ethic; to dedicate themselves to the prevention of accident-injuries. The roots of the unsafe-vehicle problem are so entrenched that the situation can be improved only by the forging of new instruments of citizen action. When thirty practicing physicians picketed for safe auto design at the New York International Automobile Show on April 7, 1965, their unprecedented action was the measure of their desperation over the inaction of the men and institutions in government and industry who have failed to provide the public with the vehicle safety to which it is entitled. The picketing surgeons, orthopedists, pediatricians, and general practitioners marched in protest because the existing medical, legal, and engineering organizations have defaulted.

from Ralph Nader, *Unsafe at Any Speed: The Designed-In Dangers of the American Automobile* (New York: Grossman, 1965).

Research Options

1. Use a resource such as *The World Almanac and Book of Facts* or *Statistical Abstract of the United States* to gather recent statistics on highway fatalities. Find out whether the situation that Nader described in this excerpt has improved.

2. Research the immediate impact of Nader's report on the automobile industry as well as the long-term results. Are cars safer today? If so, why? Discuss your findings with your classmates.

CHAPTER

20

Section 2

LITERATURE SELECTION *from* Paper Wings
by Marly Swick

Twelve-year-old Suzanne Keller, the narrator of Paper Wings, comes of age during a turbulent time in our nation's history. As you read this excerpt from the novel, think about the different reactions of Suzanne's mother, her classmates, her teachers, and her bus driver on the day that President John F. Kennedy was assassinated.

Lee Harvey Oswald might as well have shot my mother through the heart. Sometimes in my confused memories of those days, when I try to reconstruct my mother's erratic behavior after the assassination, I see Jackie's face—disbelieving and devastated behind her black veil—instead of my mother's Scandinavian paleness and crumpled Kleenexes. I was only twelve at the time and there is no clear division in my memory between the public and the private world; to me, the public world was part of our household, a sort of light show emanating from our Magnavox console sitting in the corner of the family room, a backdrop to our daily lives. As far as I was concerned, our family might just as well have been riding through Dallas in that black open-air limousine, the bright sun shining, surrounded by useless Secret Service agents. My own version, if you will, of the single bullet theory.

Over the years, standing in line at various supermarkets, I would read those *National Enquirer* stories claiming that Kennedy was still alive. A vegetable in a wheelchair on a Greek island. Or a prisoner of Castro's in Cuba. And I would imagine, for an instant, my parents still married, celebrating what would have been their fortieth, their fiftieth wedding anniversary, having successfully weathered one crisis after another side by side—instead of what really happened. I recognized in those tabloid headlines my own inextinguishable desire to rewrite history. To imagine, at least, some weak flicker of that one brief shining spot having endured in the darkness of obscurity. We were, after all, a generation raised on happy endings. War was Bob Hope entertaining the troops. Marriage was Lucy and Ricky. Old age was Jimmy Durante—"Goodnight, Mrs. Calabash, wherever you are." Disease, death, disaster happened on the

> *Over the years, standing in line at various supermarkets, I would read those National Enquirer stories claiming that Kennedy was still alive.*

news to foreigners in foreign clothes speaking foreign languages.

The day that Kennedy was shot they sent us home from school early. I was standing in the girls' locker room, having just changed into my blue gym suit, when the principal's voice crackled over the intercom, solemnly informing us that the President was dead. The locker room smelled of sweat and wet towels and sickly-sweet deodorants. I felt sick to my stomach and scared as I put my camel-hair coat on without bothering to change back into my school clothes. The usual shrill bouquet of girls' voices had withered. A couple of girls spoke in hushed tones, but most of us just stood there silently, too shocked to open our mouths.

When I walked outside, the cold blast of November air felt good after the steamy, overheated locker room. The yellow school buses were lined up by the curb waiting for us. As I stood in line I took a couple of deep breaths and the nausea passed. There was snow on the ground melting into my white sneakers with my last name, "KELLER," printed in Magic Marker on the rubber heels. My legs were bare except for white popcorn anklets. I started to shiver. The bus driver opened the doors, and we filed onto the bus. The boys didn't push and shove and call out insults the way they usually did. I could see that Mrs. Sparks, the bus driver, had been crying. Usually she barked orders at us; today she just stared out the windshield as if we weren't even there. I remembered that during the campaign she had worn a Nixon-Lodge button on her plaid lumber jacket, but she seemed sad anyway. The bus was almost full. An eighth-grade girl I didn't know sat down in the empty seat next to me and whispered something to her friend in the seat in front of her. Usually I sat with Kim, but she had stayed home with a cold that day. I clutched my skirt and sweater and tights into a warm ball in my lap and felt lonely. As the bus pulled away from the curb, my English teacher, Mrs. Ritchie, smiled and waved at me and I waved back. She had a clump of pink Kleenex clutched in her hand. When I turned my head around a second later, she was sobbing and the handsome new shop teacher, Mr. McDuffy, had his arm around her shoulders. In class that morning, right before gym, I had given a book report on *The Story of My Life* by Helen Keller, and as the disquietingly quiet bus pulled away from the curb, I recited to myself the sentences of the report I had learned by heart and my cheeks burned as I remembered how the boys in the class had laughed when I read aloud the first letter Helen had ever written to her mother, which I thought was very touching: "Helen will write mother letter paper did give helen medicine mildred will sit in swing mildred did kiss helen teacher did give helen peach george is sick in bed george arm is hurt anna did give helen lemonade dog did stand up." My mother's married name happened to be Helen Keller, so I had always felt a special personal connection to her, as if we were distantly related.

The bus wheezed and groaned along Nokomis Road. As we got closer to our neighborhood, I wondered if my mother had heard the news yet. She didn't usually listen to the news until Walter Cronkite. She might not know. I didn't want to be the one to tell her. My mother loved Kennedy. I hoped my sister would get home first.

"You're Bonnie Keller's sister, right?" the eighth-grader asked, suddenly turning her attention to me.

I nodded. My sister was a senior, a cheerleader, and I could tell that this girl, overweight with mousey hair, thought of Bonnie as distant royalty.

"Is she still going with Roger Branstead?"

"Yeah."

The girl let out a dreamy peasant girl's sigh.

I shrugged. Behind his back my father and I referred to him as Roger Braindead.

The girl leaned forward and whispered something to her friend, who whispered something back.

The bus wheezed and groaned along Nokomis Road. As we got closer to our neighborhood, I wondered if my mother had heard the news yet.

They seemed to have forgotten all about the President. I glanced across the aisle at Keith Matsumi. His eyes were closed and he was clutching his black violin case against his rib cage, a serious but serene expression on his face, as if he were listening to some sad, majestic music composed by someone long dead. He opened his eyes and I looked away. Two years earlier, in fifth grade, his mother had come to our class and taught us how to make origami Christmas tree ornaments: red and green paper birds. Most kids acted bored and embarrassed when their parents came to school—especially their mothers—but Keith had looked proud and respectful. The bus turned onto Mountain Laurel Drive and wheezed to a halt at the corner. I said "Excuse me" and crawled over the girl and clambered off the bus along with Denise DiNardo, Kevin Crawford, Keith Matsumi, and the Dinsmore twins, Ricky and Robby. The boys walked off together. I took Denise's hand—she had just started second grade and I baby-sat for her sometimes. She looked confused and frightened, as if she realized that something bad had happened but didn't know what.

"The President died," I told her as we walked toward her house, which was just on the other side of the Quaves' house. "He was shot," I explained, as if trying to explain it to myself. It still didn't seem real. Her mittened hand grabbed mine tighter and she started to cry.

"Is my daddy hurt?" she asked.

"No," I said, "your father's perfectly okay. There's nothing to worry about. This is just something far away. In Washington, D.C."

Mrs. DiNardo saw us coming and opened the front door holding Denise's four-year-old sister, Dianne, in her arms. Denise ran up the neatly shoveled walkway and grabbed her mother around the waist, crying, even though she didn't know what about. I turned around and headed across the street to my house. It looked just as it had that morning when I'd left for school. You couldn't tell that anything had changed. At the front door I cupped my hands and peered in through the glass. It didn't look as if my sister was home yet. Her coat wasn't hanging on its hook in the hallway. I couldn't see my mother, but I could hear the TV. I opened the door, hung my coat up, set my books and clothes down on the hall table, and followed the sound of the television into the family room. My mother was sitting on the floor in front of our TV set, crying into a bath towel. Her hair was wet and soapy. She was wearing a white brassiere and black slacks. Apparently she had been washing her hair in the kitchen sink, something she did twice a week, when Kim's mother knocked on the back door with the news. It was chilly in the family room—I could see goose bumps on my mother's arms—but she seemed oblivious to the fact that she was half naked and trickles of water were running off her neck and onto the carpet. When she looked up and saw me standing there, she caught her breath and bit her lip until she stopped crying. Then she took a deep, deep breath and said, "This is the worst thing that has ever happened."

I took a couple of steps closer to her and patted her awkwardly on the shoulder, trying to think of something to say. On the television screen Vice President Johnson was taking the oath of office. Jackie's nylons were splattered with blood and her hand rested on the coffin next to her. I walked over and changed the channel. As if maybe it was just a sad movie. A real tearjerker. "What are you doing?" my mother asked. I didn't answer her. Back then we only got three channels. It was the same picture on all three stations. That's how I knew it was real.

Activity Options

1. With a small group of classmates, do an oral history project about Kennedy's assassination. Conduct interviews with adult family members and others in your community to collect their recollections and reactions to this national tragedy. Before you begin this activity, draw up a list of questions, such as "Where were you when you heard the news that Kennedy had been shot?"

2. Mrs. Keller—as well as other characters in this passage—are devastated by the assassination of President Kennedy. What recent historical event made a deep impression on you? Why? Write a brief personal narrative about this event. Share your narrative with the class.

3. The following chart describes various emotional reactions to grief. Study the chart. Then discuss with classmates which characters exhibit these different reactions and why you think so many Americans were greatly affected by Kennedy's death.

Shock and disbelief	**Guilt**
Emotional release, such as crying	**Hostility and resentment**
Depression and loneliness	**Dejection**
Physical distress	**Reconciliation**
Panic	**Adaptation**

CHAPTER 20

Section 2

AMERICAN LIVES Alan Shepard

Space Explorer Who Restored Confidence

"It's a beautiful day. Boy, what a ride!"—Alan Shepard's first words on returning to Earth after his space flight, 1961

Alan Shepard (b. 1923) was the first American in space and the fifth person to walk on the moon. He helped to restore Americans' confidence in the space program.

While he was in the Navy, Shepard became fascinated with flying. He wanted to win his flight wings so badly that along with naval flight training he also took civilian flying courses. He became a pilot in 1947 and three years later a test pilot—a sometimes dangerous calling.

Soon after the Soviet Union embarrassed the United States by orbiting the first artificial satellite in 1957, the National Aeronautics and Space Administration (NASA) decided that America needed to be first to orbit a human. NASA sent letters to the top test pilots inviting them to apply for the program. Shepard joined the program and after months of testing was named as one of the first seven astronauts in Project Mercury.

For the next two years, the astronauts took classes in astronomy, astrophysics, and biology. They endured constant physical tests. They patiently suffered through experiments that checked their responses to weightlessness and high gravity. They smiled through countless press conferences and public appearances. Finally, Shepard was chosen to take the first flight.

Then Americans had a crisis of confidence. In April 1961, the Soviet Union rocketed Yuri Gagarin into space. Americans were embarrassed once again by the Soviet Union's space superiority. NASA looked inept—especially later in the month when it had to blow up two rockets that were not working correctly. On top of these disasters, Shepard's flight had to be canceled because of bad weather. Nothing, it seemed, was going right.

Finally, on May 5, 1961, the weather was cooperative. Shepard was strapped into the capsule just after five in the morning. Problems forced a delay in the countdown, however. Finally, Shepard's irritated voice came over the radio to the engineers. "Why don't you fix your little problem . . . and light

this candle." At 9:34 the rocket ignited, and Shepard was lifted into space. He returned to Earth fifteen minutes later. His flight was not as impressive as Gagarin's orbit of the earth, but Americans were thrilled. Shepard was treated like a hero. He was given a medal by President Kennedy and a huge parade by New York City. Twenty days later, the President used his success as the occasion for a new goal: to land an American on the moon.

Shepard hoped to fly a spacecraft again. It seemed as though he would get his wish in 1963 when he was named to the Gemini program, the Project Mercury successor. However, Shepard had developed an inner-ear problem that caused him dizziness in the air. Shepard stayed with NASA as an administrator, but he was not allowed to fly.

Five years later, Shepard had surgery to repair his ear problem. He then joined the Apollo program, which aimed at landing on the moon. NASA enjoyed success with two moon landings in 1969. Then, in 1970, disaster hit when equipment problems forced NASA to abort the Apollo 13 lunar landing and three astronauts almost died in space. Clouds returned to the U.S. space effort.

Once again, though, Shepard eased Americans' concerns. His Apollo 14 flight in 1971 was flawless. At age 47, he became the oldest American to fly in space and the fifth to walk on the moon. The mission proceeded so smoothly that, during his moon walk, Shepard hit a few golf balls. In 1974 Shepard resigned from the space program and the Navy and went into private life.

Questions

1. The first seven astronauts were given constant media attention? Why?
2. From two hours before liftoff until after the recovery of his space capsule, Shepard's first flight was broadcast live. Why would the government allow that?
3. Do you think landing a person on the moon was a worthwhile goal? Why or why not?

CHAPTER
20
Section 3

AMERICAN LIVES Rachel Carson
Pioneering Writer of Science

"[W]e should no longer accept the counsel of those who tell us we must fill our world with poisonous chemicals. We should look about and see what other course is open to us."—Rachel Carson, Silent Spring (1962)

Rachel Carson (1907–1964) was a talented writer who cared deeply for nature. Fearing for the safety of the natural world, she wrote a book that helped launch the environmental movement.

Carson always wanted to be a writer. In college, though, she took a biology course that fascinated her, and she switched her major from English. After additional study, Carson taught science. Faced with the need to support her mother and two orphaned nieces, she took a job with the Bureau of Fisheries in 1936. At the urging of others, she submitted to a magazine an article she had written for the bureau, and it was accepted. A publisher then asked Carson to expand the piece into a book. The result, *Under the Sea-Wind* (1941), "a naturalist's picture of ocean life," was praised but did not sell well to a public suddenly worried about world war.

It was ten years before Carson could publish her second book, *The Sea Around Us.* Praised for its science and poetic exploration of the oceans' mysteries, the book was a bestseller. More important, the book's financial success—and a fellowship she was awarded—allowed Carson to resign her job and write full time. In 1955 she published her third book, *The Edge of the Sea*, a study of Atlantic Coast seashores.

Soon Carson undertook another project—one that would have profound effect on American attitudes. A friend of Carson had a bird sanctuary on her property. Following state law, it had been sprayed with DDT, a pesticide. Her friend noticed that birds were dying in large numbers. She asked Carson to help put a stop to the use of DDT. In her old government job, Carson had read disturbing reports about DDT. With this new evidence of its dangers, she resolved to write about it.

DDT had been discovered by a Swiss chemist in 1939. It was an excellent killer of insects. During World War II, DDT use prevented disease among soldiers and refugees. After the war, DDT helped save millions of lives by killing mosquitoes that carry malaria. However, DDT had problems, too. It could not be washed off food, and it could build up to dangerous levels in animals' and humans' bodies over time. Also, insects were acquiring resistance to DDT. That meant that larger doses would be needed to kill them. Those larger doses were more dangerous to animals and humans. Still, most people of the day knew only of DDT's successes. It seemed like a miracle chemical.

For years, Carson read scientific reports about DDT and worked on a fourth book. She found that DDT sprayed on a Michigan college campus to destroy bugs had also killed all the local robins. She learned that DDT was responsible for the declining numbers of many bird species—including the national bird, the bald eagle. Finally, in 1962, she published the now-classic *Silent Spring.*

Carson's book was subjected to a storm of criticism from chemical companies. She was called "hysterical," and her book, they said, should be ignored. The public, though, was disturbed by Carson's claims—which she had backed with research. President Kennedy called for a special commission to investigate. It agreed that DDT was dangerous, and by 1969, the government was phasing out most uses of the pesticide.

Carson's book had even more wide-ranging consequences. She demonstrated that people were affected by whatever affected nature. Americans' thinking changed as a result, and many people were drawn into environmental work. Carson died from cancer less than two years after *Silent Spring* was published, but she lived long enough to know she had made the desired impact.

Questions

1. How did public attitudes to DDT make it difficult for Carson to convince people of its dangers?
2. What did Carson mean when she titled her book *Silent Spring*?
3. Why did chemical companies attack Carson for *Silent Spring*?

Name _____ Date _____

CHAPTER
21
Section 1

GUIDED READING *Taking on Segregation*

As you read, answer questions about important events in the civil rights movement.

1875	Civil Rights Act is passed.	→

1. What did the Civil Rights Act of 1875 do?

1883	Supreme Court rules 1875 Civil Rights Act unconstitutional.	
1896	*Plessy* v. *Ferguson*	→

2. How did the Court rule in *Plessy*?

1945	World War II ends.	→

3. In what three ways did World War II help set the stage for the modern civil rights movement?

1946	*Morgan* v. *Virginia* outlaws mandatory segregation on interstate buses.

a.

b.

1950	*Sweat* v. *Painter* declares that state law schools must admit black applicants.

c.

4. Who argued *Brown*'s case?

5. What did the *Brown* ruling declare?

1954	*Brown* v. *Board of Education*	→
1955	Supreme Court orders school desegregation.	
	Emmett Till is murdered.	

	Rosa Parks is arrested.	→

6. What organization was formed to support Rosa Parks?

7. What did it do?

1956	Supreme Court outlaws bus segregation.
1957	Little Rock faces school desegregation crisis. →

8. How did President Eisenhower respond to the Little Rock crisis?

	Southern Christian Leadership Conference (SCLC) is formed. →

9. Who was the president of SCLC?

10. What was SCLC's purpose?

1960	Student Nonviolent Coordination Committee (SNCC) is formed. →

11. What did SNCC accomplish, and how?

Name _____ Date _____

CHAPTER 21

Section 2

GUIDED READING *The Triumphs of a Crusade*

A. As you read this section, take notes to answer the questions about the time line.

1961	Freedom riders travel through the South. →	1. What was the goal of the freedom riders?	2. What was the Kennedy administration's response?
1962	James Meredith integrates Ole Miss.		
1963	Birmingham and the University of Alabama are integrated.		
	Kennedy sends civil rights bill to Congress.		
	Medgar Evers is murdered.	3. What was the goal of the march on Washington?	4. Who attended the march?
	March on Washington →		
	Birmingham church bombing kills four girls.	5. What was the goal of the Freedom Summer project?	6. Who volunteered for the project?
	Kennedy is assassinated.		
1964	Freedom Summer →		
	Three civil rights workers are murdered.	7. What role did the violence shown on television play in this march?	8. What did the march encourage President Johnson to do?
	Civil Rights Act is passed.		
1965	March from Selma to Montgomery →		
	Voting Rights Act is passed. →	9. What did the Voting Rights Act outlaw?	10. What did the law accomplish?

B. On the back of this paper, explain **Fannie Lou Hamer**'s role in the civil rights movement.

Name _____ Date _____

A. As you read this section, make notes to answer the questions.

1. What is the main difference between de facto and de jure segregation?
2. How did the ideas of SNCC differ from those of the Nation of Islam?
3. How did the early views of Malcolm X differ from his later ideas?
4. What changes took place in Stokely Carmichael's membership in civil rights organizations?
5. How did the ideas of SNCC differ from those of the Black Panthers?

6. What gains were made by the civil rights and Black Power movements? Identify four.

a.	b.	c.	d.

B. On the back of this paper, briefly explain what changes or reforms each of the following
called for: **Black Power,** the **Kerner Commission,** and the **Civil Rights Act of 1968.**

CHAPTER 21

BUILDING VOCABULARY *Civil Rights*

A. Matching Match the description in the second column with the term or name in the first column. Write the appropriate letter next to the word.

_____ 1. Civil Rights Act of 1964   a. militant African-American political party

_____ 2. affirmative action   b. form of protest against segregation

_____ 3. Nation of Islam   c. actions sparked Montgomery bus boycott

_____ 4. Martin Luther King, Jr.   d. banned discrimination in public places

_____ 5. Black Panthers   e. tried to desegregate interstate bus travel

_____ 6. Rosa Parks   f. most prominent civil rights leader

_____ 7. freedom riders   g. members known as Black Muslims

_____ 8. sit-in   h. programs that seek to aid minorities

B. Completion Select the term or name that best completes the sentence.

literacy tests   churches   James Meredith
schools   Warren Commission   Kerner Commission
Stokely Carmichael   poll tax   freedom summer

1. The effort to register African Americans in the South to vote was known as _____.

2. The Voting Rights Act of 1965 eliminated the so-called _____, which had disqualified many African-American voters in the past.

3. _____ was one of the most prominent voices of the Black Power movement.

4. Appointed by President Johnson to study the cause of urban violence, the _____ blamed much of the problem on white racism.

5. In the case *Brown* v. *Board of Education of Topeka*, the Supreme Court struck down segregated _____ as unconstitutional.

C. Writing Write a paragraph incorporating the following terms:

de facto segregation   **de jure segregation**

CHAPTER

21

Section 1

SKILLBUILDER PRACTICE *Making Inferences*

In September 1957, Elizabeth Eckford made history as she forced her way through an angry crowd of whites in an effort to integrate Central High School in Little Rock, Arkansas. Study the photo of Eckford on page 703 of the text and read the news article on this page. Consider what inferences you can make about the impact of this event. Then answer the questions that follow. (See Skillbuilder Handbook, p. R10.)

Hazel Bryan was part of the crowd that day [in September 1957]. Her face grimaced in hate, she shouted at Eckford, who clutched her books to her chest and walked on, her emotions hidden behind dark glasses.

When a photograph of the bitter meeting between the two 15-year-old girls appeared in newspapers around the country, Eckford became a symbol of the civil rights movement. Bryan's young face became an image of racial hatred.

Now 55, the women met . . . for the first time since that troubled time. There were smiles and poses for pictures. They mostly let the past be.

"Thank you, Elizabeth, for agreeing to do this," Bryan, now Hazel Massery, said quietly as she greeted Eckford at her home.

Answered Eckford, before the two left for the school: "I think you're very brave to face the cameras again. . . ."

At the school, both black and white students recognized Eckford. "Miss Eckford, I just want you to know how much I respect you," a black student said. A white junior high student gave Eckford a big hello; they talked briefly about taking classes at the high school.

Massery said that she had hoped others would know of her regret and her acknowledgment that intolerance was wrong.

"I just want to say, Elizabeth, I'm elated that you're doing this," she said. "I'd like for my children to be proud, to see that both of us are role models."

Peggy Harris, *Associated Press* writer, Tuesday, September 23, 1997

1. By studying the photo on page 703, what can you infer about the obstacles facing Eckford and the other African-American students who integrated Central High School?

_____

_____

2. By comparing the photo with the news story, what can you infer about reasons African Americans consider Litttle Rock a milestone in the civil rights movement?

_____

_____

CHAPTER

21

Section 1

RETEACHING ACTIVITY *Taking on Segregation*

Finding Main Ideas

The following questions deal with the beginnings of the civil rights movement.
Answer them in the space provided.

1. How were the Supreme Court cases *Plessy* v. *Ferguson* and *Brown* v. *Board of Education
of Topeka* related?

_____

_____

2. How did President Eisenhower respond to the Little Rock school crisis?

_____

_____

3. How did the Montgomery Bus Boycott begin? What effect did it have?

_____

_____

4. What was significant about the Civil Rights Act of 1957? What did it accomplish?

_____

_____

5. What was Martin Luther King, Jr.'s approach to battling racial injustice?

_____

_____

6. How did the sit-in demonstrations throughout the South reflect King's approach?

_____

_____

RETEACHING ACTIVITY *Triumph of a Crusade*

Summarizing

Complete the chart below by explaining how each of the entries promoted the cause of the civil rights and greater equality for African Americans.

Occurrence	Significance
Freedom rides	
March on Birmingham	
Civil Rights Act of 1964	
24th Amendment	
March on Selma	
Voting Rights Act of 1965	

CHAPTER 21 Section 3

RETEACHING ACTIVITY *Challenges and Changes in the Movement*

Completion

Choose the best answer for each item. Write the letter of your answer in the blank.

_____ 1. The civil rights leader who preached that blacks should separate from white society was
   a. Martin Luther King, Jr.
   b. James Meredith.
   c. Malcolm X.
   d. Fannie Lou Hamer.

_____ 2. The Kerner Commission blamed much of the rioting that plagued Northern cities during the mid-1960s on
   a. white racism.
   b. television violence.
   c. lax police policies.
   d. militant African Americans.

_____ 3. The Civil Rights Act of 1968 ended discrimination in
   a. housing.
   b. schools.
   c. churches.
   d. restaurants.

_____ 4. The nation experienced the worst urban rioting in its history in the days following the assassination of
   a. John F. Kennedy.
   b. Robert Kennedy.
   c. Malcolm X.
   d. Martin Luther King, Jr..

_____ 5. Civil Rights leaders criticized the fact that much of the money for President Johnson's War on Poverty had been redirected to help fund
   a. the space program.
   b. the Vietnam War.
   c. medical research.
   d. expressway construction.

_____ 6. Between 1965 and 1992 the number of African Americans holding elected offices grew from less than 100 to about
   a. 3,000.
   b. 7,000
   c. 10,000.
   d. 15,000.

GEOGRAPHY APPLICATION: REGION

The Brown *Decision, Ten Years Later*

Section 1

Directions: Read the paragraphs below and study the map carefully. Then answer the questions that follow.

In 1954, the Supreme Court ruled in *Brown* v. *Board of Education* that to separate public-school students "solely on the basis of race" was unconstitutional. The Court had established a "separate but equal" doctrine in 1896, in its *Plessy* v. *Ferguson* ruling, but the 1954 decision reversed that ruling. Now, the court declared that "'separate but equal' has no place" in public education.

The *Brown* decision, however, did not bring public-school segregation to an immediate end. The responsibility for implementing desegregation fell to local governments—to school officials who had to keep in mind state laws and regional customs. Thus, at times, the move toward statewide compliance took place slowly, almost one school at a time. When desegregation efforts lagged, the

Supreme Court issued a second *Brown* decision in 1955, directing lower courts to admit African-American students to public schools "with all deliberate speed." Eventually, in some areas of the South, the federal government had to step in and enforce desegregation.

Still, even ten years after *Brown,* only about 380,000 African-American elementary and secondary students in 17 Southern states and the District of Columbia—less than 11 percent of the 3.5 million students in the region—were going to schools with white students. In Alabama only 94 out of 89,000 African-American students, and in Mississippi only 58 out of 22,000 African-American students, attended integrated schools.

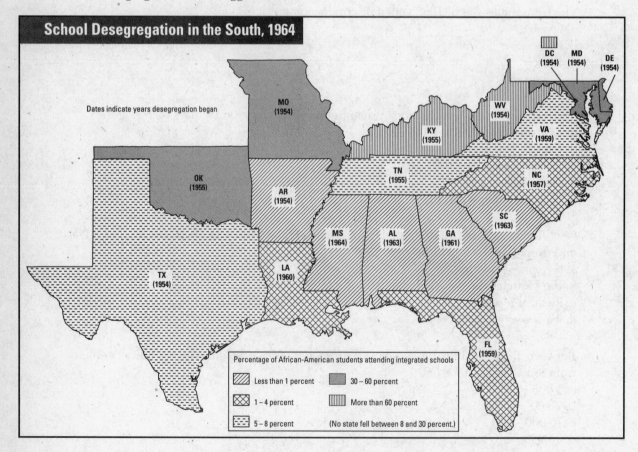

School Desegregation in the South, 1964

Dates indicate years desegregation began

DC (1954) MD (1954) DE (1954)
MO (1954)
WV (1954)
KY (1955)
VA (1959)
OK (1955)
AR (1954)
TN (1955)
NC (1957)
SC (1963)
MS (1964)   AL (1963)   GA (1961)
LA (1960)
TX (1954)
FL (1959)

Percentage of African-American students attending integrated schools

Less than 1 percent   30 – 60 percent
1 – 4 percent   More than 60 percent
5 – 8 percent   (No state fell between 8 and 30 percent.)

Interpreting Text and Visuals

1. Which states in the region shown on the map began to integrate their public schools in the year of the *Brown* v. *Board of Education* decision? (Do not count the District of Columbia.) _____
_____

2. In which states did school desegregation not begin until the 1960s? _____
_____

3. What generalization can you make about the relationship between the time a state began the desegregation process and the degree of integration of its schools in 1964? _____
_____
_____

   Which state is a glaring exception to that trend? _____

4. In which states were 30 to 60 percent of African-American students in integrated schools? _____
_____

5. In which states was the percentage of African-American students in integrated schools less than the region's average? _____
_____
_____

6. Which five of the states you listed for question 5 had percentages the farthest below the regional average? _____
_____

   How might the economic and social history of those five states have led to a resistance to desegregation? _____
_____
_____
_____

CHAPTER 21

Section 1

PRIMARY SOURCE Crisis in Little Rock

When 16-year-old Elizabeth Eckford left for Little Rock's Central High School in September 1957, she did not know that the governor had ordered the National Guard to keep her and eight other black students from entering the all-white school. This is Eckford's account of her first day at an integrated school.

Before I left home Mother called us into the living room. She said we should have a word of prayer. Then I caught the bus and got off a block from the school. I saw a large crowd of people standing across the street from the soldiers guarding Central. As I walked on, the crowd suddenly got very quiet. Superintendent Blossom had told us to enter by the front door. I looked at all the people and thought, "Maybe I will be safer if I walk down the block to the front entrance behind the guards."

At the corner I tried to pass through the long line of guards around the school so as to enter the grounds behind them. One of the guards pointed across the street. So I pointed in the same direction and asked whether he meant for me to cross the street and walk down. He nodded "yes." So, I walked across the street conscious of the crowd that stood there, but they moved away from me.

For a moment all I could hear was the shuffling of their feet. Then someone shouted, "Here she comes, get ready!" I moved away from the crowd on the sidewalk and into the street. . . .

The crowd moved in closer and then began to follow me, calling me names. I still wasn't afraid. Just a little bit nervous. Then my knees started to shake all of a sudden and I wondered whether I could make it to the center entrance a block away. It was the longest block I ever walked in my whole life.

Even so, I still wasn't too scared because all the time I kept thinking that the guards would protect me.

When I got right in front of the school, I went up to a guard again. But this time he just looked straight ahead and didn't move to let me pass him. I didn't know what to do. Then I looked and saw that the path leading to the front entrance was a little further ahead. So I walked until I was right in front of the path to the front door.

I stood looking at the school—it looked so big! Just then the guards let some white students go through.

The crowd was quiet. I guess they were waiting to see what was going to happen. When I was able to steady my knees, I walked up to the guard who had

let the white students in. He too didn't move. When I tried to squeeze past him, he raised his bayonet and then the other guards closed in and they raised their bayonets.

They glared at me with a mean look and I was very frightened and didn't know what to do. I turned around and the crowd came toward me.

They moved closer and closer. Somebody started yelling, "Lynch her! Lynch her!"

I tried to see a friendly face somewhere in the mob—someone who maybe would help. I looked into the face of an old woman and it seemed a kind face, but when I looked at her again, she spat on me.

They came closer, shouting, "No nigger bitch is going to get in our school. Get out of here!"

I turned back to the guards but their faces told me I wouldn't get help from them. Then I looked down the block and saw a bench at the bus stop. I thought, "If I can only get there I will be safe." I don't know why the bench seemed a safe place. . . .

When I finally got there, I don't think I could have gone another step. I sat down and the mob crowded up and began shouting all over again. Someone hollered, "Drag her over to this tree! Let's take care of the nigger." Just then a white man sat down beside me, put his arm around me and patted my shoulder. He raised my chin and said, "Don't let them see you cry."

Then, a white lady—she was very nice—she came over to me on the bench. She spoke to me but I don't remember now what she said. She put me on the bus and sat next to me. . . . [T]he next thing I remember I was standing in front of the School for the Blind, where Mother works.

from William Loren Katz, *Eyewitness: The Negro in American History* (New York: Pitman, 1967), 492–494.

Discussion Question

Why do you think Elizabeth Eckford encountered such a hostile reaction when she arrived at Central High School? Cite evidence from your textbook to support your opinion.

CHAPTER 21

Section 2

PRIMARY SOURCE Civil Rights Song

"We Shall Overcome," the anthem of the civil rights movement, derives from an African-American hymn that was written in the early 1900s by Reverend C. A. Tindley. Later brought by South Carolina tobacco workers to Highlander Folk School in the Tennessee mountains, the hymn was first adapted for protest and sung in support of the 1930s labor movement.

We Shall Overcome

We shall overcome,
      we shall overcome,
We shall overcome some day.
Oh, deep in my heart, I do believe,
We shall overcome some day.

We are not afraid,
      we are not afraid,
We are not afraid today.
Oh, deep in my heart, I do believe,
We shall overcome some day.

We are not alone,
      we are not alone,
We are not alone today.
Oh, deep in my heart, I do believe,
We shall overcome some day.

The truth will make us free,
      the truth will make us free.
The truth will make us free some day.
Oh, deep in my heart, I do believe,
We shall overcome some day.

We'll walk hand in hand,
      we'll walk hand in hand,
We'll walk hand in hand some day.
Oh, deep in my heart, I do believe,
We shall overcome some day.

The Lord will see us through,
      the Lord will see us through,
The Lord will see us through today.
Oh, deep in my heart, I do believe,
We shall overcome some day.

from *We Shall Overcome! Songs of the Southern Freedom Movement* compiled by Guy and Candie Carawan for The Student Nonviolent Coordinating Committee, Oak Publications.

Activity Options

1. Listen to a recording of this song or perform the song with classmates. If possible, have classmates who play musical instruments accompany you as you sing. Then discuss your response to the song and why you think it became the best-known protest song of the civil rights movement.

2. Listen to recordings of other civil rights songs such as "Keep Your Eyes on the Prize," "This Little Light of Mine," "Ain't Gonna Let Nobody Turn Me Round," "We Shall Not Be Moved," and "I'm Gonna Sit at the Welcome Table." Then compare and contrast these songs with "We Shall Overcome" in terms of lyrics, tempo, melody, and rhythm.

CHAPTER 21

Section 2

PRIMARY SOURCE *from* **"I Have a Dream"**
by Martin Luther King, Jr.

On August 28, 1963, more than 250,000 people took part in a march on Washington, D.C., in support of the civil rights bill. As you read this part of the speech that Dr. King delivered that day, think about his dream and whether it has come true.

I say to you today, my friends, even though we face the difficulties of today and tomorrow, I still have a dream. It is a dream deeply rooted in the American dream. I have a dream that one day this nation will rise up and live out the true meaning of its creed, "We hold these truths to be self-evident; that all men are created equal." I have a dream that one day on the red hills of Georgia, sons of former slaves and the sons of former slave owners will be able to sit down together at the table of brotherhood. I have a dream that one day even the state of Mississippi, a state sweltering with the heat of injustice, sweltering with the heat of oppression, will be transformed into an oasis of freedom and justice. I have a dream that my four little children will one day live in a nation where they will not be judged by the color of their skin, but by the content of their character.

I have a dream today!

I have a dream that one day down in Alabama—with its vicious racists, with its Governor having his lips dripping with the words of interposition and nullification—one day right there in Alabama, little black boys and black girls will be able to join hands with little white boys and white girls as sisters and brothers.

I have a dream today!

I have a dream that one day every valley shall be exalted, and every hill and mountain shall be made low. The rough places will be plain and the crooked places will be made straight, "and the glory of the Lord shall be revealed, and all flesh shall see it together."

This is our hope. This is the faith that I go back to the South with. With this faith we will be able to hew out of the mountain of despair a stone of hope. With this faith we will be able to transform the jangling discords of our nation into a beautiful symphony of brotherhood. With this faith we will be able to work together, to pray together, to struggle together, to go to jail together, to stand up for freedom together, knowing that we will be free one day. And this will be the day. This will be the day when all of God's children will be able to sing with new meaning, "My country 'tis of thee, sweet land of liberty, of thee I sing. Land where my fathers died, land of the pilgrims' pride, from every mountainside, let freedom ring." And if America is to be a great nation, this must become true.

So let freedom ring from the prodigious hilltops of New Hampshire, let freedom ring from the mighty mountains of New York; let freedom ring from the heightening Alleghenies of Pennsylvania; let freedom ring from the snow-capped Rockies of Colorado; let freedom ring from the curvaceous slopes of California. But not only that. Let freedom ring from Stone Mountain of Georgia; let freedom ring from Lookout Mountain of Tennessee; let freedom ring from every hill and molehill of Mississippi. "From every mountainside, let freedom ring."

And when this happens, and when we allow freedom to ring, when we let it ring from every village and every hamlet, from every state and every city, we will be able to speed up that day when all of God's children—black men and white men, Jews and Gentiles, Protestants and Catholics—will be able to join hands and sing in the words of the old Negro spiritual, "Free at last. Free at last. Thank God Almighty, we are free at last."

Discussion Questions

1. What does Dr. King mean when he says he has a dream that the nation "will live out the true meaning of its creed"?
2. What criticisms does King level at American society?
3. Do you think that King's dream has been fulfilled? Explain your response.

CHAPTER

21

Section 2

PRIMARY SOURCE Political Poster

During the Freedom Summer of 1964, hundreds of civil rights volunteers, both black and white, converged on Mississippi to conduct voter registration drives. This is one of their posters.

We Shall Overcome Register-Vote Poster. Schomburg Center for Research in Black Culture, Art and Artifacts Division, The New York Public Library, Astor, Lenox and Tilden Foundations.

Discussion Questions

1. What images and slogans does this poster use to persuade African Americans to register to vote?
2. Which images or slogans do you think are most persuasive?

3. If you were to design a poster for Freedom Summer, what images or slogans would you use? Take into consideration what you have learned about the project and about the opposition that civil rights activists faced.

CHAPTER 21

Section 2

LITERATURE SELECTION *from And All Our Wounds Forgiven*
by Julius Lester

This novel, about a fictional civil rights leader named John Calvin (Cal) Marshall, his wife, Andrea, his aide, Lisa, and his chief lieutenant, Robert (Bobby) Card, gives an insider's view of the civil rights movement. As you read this excerpt, think about the dangers that civil rights workers faced.

He was 19. If he had known how young that was, he would not have left school. He certainly would not have gone to Shiloh where the general store/post office on the short main street, a white diner/bar and a colored one across the street were the only visible sign of the community scattered along dusty streets and roads and through the cotton fields owned by Jeb Lincoln.

"There's a man named Charlie Montgomery in Shiloh who has been trying to get the Negroes to register to vote."

"But what am I supposed to do when I get there?" he'd asked Cal.

Cal smiled ruefully. "We're all new at this civil rights stuff, Robert. You talk to people and you listen. When it comes time to do, either they or you will know what." . . .

He went. The first week no one spoke to him, not even Charlie Montgomery. Why should they have? He wasn't one of them. The car in which he had driven into town could also take him away at the first sign of trouble.

Anybody could come to town and talk about freedom and registering to vote. Hell, every colored person in Mississippi knew they should be free and able to vote. That wasn't news. What they needed was to be convinced there was a way, and even if it meant wading up a bloody stream without hip boots, they needed someone to show them how to keep their balance while treading on slippery rocks. They needed someone to show them who they could be. They knew who they were.

Bobby's words would make little difference. Their literacy was in the ways of people. So, he sat on their front porches and chatted about the weather and the cotton, and with the older ones he commiserated about the errancies of the younger generation, and with the impatient youth he commiserated about the

> **"We're all new at this civil rights stuff, Robert. You talk to people and you listen. When it comes time to do, either they or you will know what."**

blindness of the old.

Finally, one day a big man blacker than suffering, wearing coveralls and a straw cowboy hat, came up to him as he sat in The Pink Teacup, the colored cafe, and said, "I'm Charlie Montgomery." He stuck out a hand big enough to have grasped Robert's entire head, and Robert Card had found a home in Shiloh, Mississippi.

World War II had changed Charlie. "I felt like some kind of fool over there in Europe getting shot at defending a country that was killing niggers everyday. I'd lie there in them foxholes, man, the Germans zinging bullets through the air, and think to myself that if I got out of there alive, I was coming back to Shiloh and do some fighting for me and mines. You understand what I'm telling you? Me and mines!" Charlie Montgomery invited him to stay in the four-room house where he lived with his wife, Ruth.

Every morning Bobby got in his car and drove over rutted, dusty plantation roads, stopping to talk to anyone he saw about starting a sharecropper's union, or registering to vote, and almost daily there was a confrontation with some white man, a plantation overseer, the sheriff, or just a good ol' boy with a wad in his cheek and a rifle in his hand. . . .

"You be careful, son," the old folks started telling him. Maybe Negroes in Shiloh knew Death so well because it lived on the outskirts of town, sitting in a shack like an old man whose intimacy with loneliness made his only comprehensible conversations the ones he had with himself. Ol' Boy, as they called him, was moving through the world that year in a new way, not only taking people with the usual cancers, heart attacks, old age, murders, car, train, plane accidents and the freakish ones you read about in the tiny fillers in the newspaper like the girl in Germany who was playing in a cemetery and a tombstone fell on her and crushed her or the Japanese fisherman killed when a swordfish leaped from the water and with its broad bill stabbed the man in the heart and returned to the water with the grace of an Olympic diver. Death seemed to take on new life because it was the consort of the change Bobby and others his age knew had to come if they were to stand erect beneath the sky and he didn't know who Patrice Lumumba was, was not even sure how to say his name and did not know what countries bordered Zaire or where it was on the map of Africa, but he did not have to know the details to understand that Huntley and Brinkley were telling him that a Negro had been assassinated because he wanted to be free. Change was in the air like the smell of winter on Thanksgiving Day.

"Man done broke the bonds of earth," Mrs. Montgomery said with Biblical accuracy one evening sitting on the porch looking at the paper. "Charlie, you see here that them Russians done sent a man into space and he circled the world from out where the stars twinkle?"

"Everybody wants to be free of what holds 'em down, even when it's gravity doing the holding."

It was Andrea Marshall who had shown him the paragraph in the *New York Times* about President Kennedy sending troops to Vietnam, another place Robert had never heard of and wasn't sure where it was but he understood instinctively that JFK didn't care a damn about freedom if he could send troops to Vietnam and not Mississippi. Every month he drove to Nashville for a day or two to see Cal and Andrea. Cal was still not so famous yet that he did not have time to sit around the kitchen table late at night, and the three of them would talk without purpose or direction, just talk and in the talking, learn.

"The United States broke relations with Cuba and banned travel there," Andrea said one night. "Why would this mighty nation be afraid of a small island? Why would it want to prevent us from traveling there? They must be afraid we'll learn something if we go there."

"Castro might know a thing or two about freedom that we don't," Cal commented.

Their distrust of Kennedy intensified when he founded the Peace Corps. "Why th' hell would he

want to send young, idealistic Americans all over the world to help the poor when he's got Negroes in Alabama and Mississippi and Georgia and Louisiana who can use all the help anybody can give 'em?"

When Cal was angry his speech returned to the well of his southern ancestry and that was where it stayed for much of the year because 1961 was when History attached its strings to his arms and legs.

Robert knew nothing of that until he sat with the Montgomerys one evening that spring watching Huntley-Brinkley on the one channel they could get on the twelve-inch screen TV their daughter had brought them from Memphis, the only TV anybody colored had in the county, which was why the living room was always filled with people, especially at 6:30 when Chet Huntley and David Brinkley were on and it got quieter for that half-hour than it did at a funeral with no one saying a word even during the commercials as if silence were needed to absorb the pictures, not the content of the images but their mere existence as representations of the world beyond the Mississippi Delta and it did not matter if the images were of the president and his beautiful wife, Jackie, on a sailboat or of Red Square in Moscow or Alan Shepard being the first American blasted into space. What was important was seeing there was other than cotton and the flat delta earth and so it was that evening in May when on the TV screen appeared the image of John Calvin Marshall being dragged from a Greyhound bus by a mob of whites in Birmingham, Alabama, and beaten within a heartskip of death, he and eleven others—colored and white—who had dared challenge the laws of segregation and sit together on a bus. They called their action "Freedom Rides," and across the South, they and anyone who worked in civil rights were thereafter known as "Freedom Riders."

And so it was that evening in May when on the TV screen appeared the image of John Calvin Marshall being dragged from a Greyhound bus by a mob of whites in Birmingham, Alabama.

Bobby had been hurt and angry Cal had not told him of the plans for the Freedom Rides, had not even hinted that such a major action was in the offing.

"Trust you?" Cal chuckled when Bobby was able to confront him after he was released from the hospital. "If I had told you about it, there is nothing I could have said or done that would've kept you away.

Am I right?"

Bobby nodded.

"What good would that have done the people in Shiloh who have come to depend on you emotionally? What would they think if you decide to jump up and go off everytime there's a bit of hot action somewhere? I sent you to Mississippi to lay the foundation for change that will continue long after you and I are gone."

The president himself pleaded with Cal not to continue the Freedom Rides into Mississippi where Cal was determined to go. Cal ignored the pleas and boarded another Greyhound bus with an integrated group and rode into Jackson, Mississippi. White Mississippi would not tolerate mob violence. The police backed a paddy wagon up to the door of the Greyhound bus. When Cal and those with him stepped off, one foot hit the pavement and the other went up and onto the steel step of the paddy wagon. Within twenty four hours they had been tried, convicted and were on their way to serving sixty days at the Mississippi State Penitentiary at Parchman, known simply as Parchman Farm.

What no one, not even Cal, could have anticipated was that the idea of the Freedom Rides caught the imagination of white college students all over the country. They began taking Greyhound buses from Chicago, Berkeley, New York, Washington, D.C., and came to Jackson, Mississippi to be arrested for trespassing, disturbing the peace and violating the laws of Mississippi, which required separation of the races. . . .

By the end of the summer of 1961, several hundred young people, white and black, had been sent to Parchman, and there the civil rights movement was truly born. Sixty days in Parchman broke the spirit of petty thieves and callous murderers, but neither the warden nor the guards nor even the other prisoners understood the spirit of freedom.

"There is nothing that can be done to the man who is not afraid to go to jail or die. Nothing! The only power any government has over its citizens is the threat of imprisonment, that is, taking away one's physical freedom, and the threat of death, that is, depriving one of life. But if when you are physically free you are imprisoned in a system that tells you where you can and can't go, who you can and can't associate with, you are not free. If you are breathing but do not have the power to define your own existence, then, you are not alive. You are free when you run into the jail cell and close the door behind you.

You are free when you look the marksman in the eye and say, 'Fire!' "

It was a sentiment Bobby heard Cal express first when he spoke at Fisk. It made sense until the afternoon almost a year and a half later when he was sitting in The Pink Teacup and someone rushed in and said there had been a shooting at the cotton gin and Bobby got in his car and drove with maniacal speed along the highway until he came to the unmarked turnoff by the railroad and as he slowed to a stop by the covered sheds where the wagon loads of cotton were brought to be ginned, he saw a large man in coveralls lying in the dust. Later, after Cal had served his sixty at Parchman, Bobby went to Nashville to see him and Andrea, to talk as they used to, just the three of them, . . . [He] tried to tell [them] what it was like to see the brains of someone you loved spilling from the skull and into the dust and how . . . flies droned in anticipation of this unexpected gift of blood and how the drone and the silence were the only sounds besides the low hum of death itself and he squatted there in the dust, alone, the white men and the black who had been working at the gin standing a respectful distance away, the murderer among them, and each of them knew who he was but no one spoke and no one moved and Bobby wondered if the murderer would raise the shotgun again and shoot him but that did not happen until finally— did an hour pass? two hours?—the sheriff came and took a blanket out of the trunk of his car and covered Charlie Montgomery, and Robert, his hands heavy with the dried and caked blood, felt released and got in his car and went to tell Ruth she was a widow lady now but she knew already.

"That man would still be alive if he hadn't let me stay in his house. That man would still be alive if not for me!" Bobby finally blurted.

"He's not going to be the last one to die," Cal told him.

"You have to get used to it. The price of freedom is death."

Research Options

1. Research a civil rights leader on whom the character John Calvin Marshall might have been modeled, such as Dr. Martin Luther King, Jr., Medger Evers, or Stokely Carmichael. Then write a report.
2. To understand the '60s references in this passage, look up Patrice Lumumba, Chet Huntley, and David Brinkley. Share your findings with the class.

CHAPTER
21

Section 1

AMERICAN LIVES ## Rosa Parks
Taking a Historic Stand by Sitting

"I didn't have any special fear. It was more of a relief to know . . . that I wasn't alone. If I was going to be fearful, it would have been as far back as I can remember, not just that separate incident."—Rosa Parks, recalling her emotions during the Montgomery bus boycott, 1988

Rosa Parks (b. 1913) has been called the mother of the civil rights movement. Her quiet act of defiance against segregation on the buses of Montgomery, Alabama, started a wave of protest in the 1950s—and launched the career of Martin Luther King, Jr.

Rosa McCauley had a difficult early life, as her parents separated and her small family struggled to live. She juggled school with work to help her family. At age 19, she married Raymond Parks, who had been active in efforts to register African Americans to vote. For the next 20 years, she worked a variety of jobs. Beginning in 1943, she was a secretary of the Montgomery chapter of the National Association for the Advancement of Colored People (NAACP). When she could, Parks protested segregation laws. She refused to use drinking fountains or elevators set aside for African Americans. She often walked home from work rather than take segregated buses.

However, on December 1, 1955, she was tired and took the bus. A white man got on the bus that day after the section reserved for whites was full. Parks and three other African Americans were told by the bus driver to give up their seats. Parks refused. "I don't think I should have to," she said. "Why do you push us around so?" The bus driver summoned police, and Parks was arrested.

Edgar Daniel Nixon—head of the local NAACP—and two lawyers paid a bond to secure Parks's release. Then Nixon asked if she would agree to appeal the case in order to challenge the segregation law. Her mother and husband feared for her safety, but she agreed to go ahead—if it will "do some good." Meanwhile, other activists in Montgomery seized on Parks's act of defiance. The Women's Political Council had been ready for months to call for a boycott of the city bus line for its segregation and rude treatment of African-American passengers. Notified of Parks's arrest, Jo Ann Robinson of the WPC issued thousands of fliers calling for the city's blacks to boycott the bus

line on December 5—the day of Parks's trial.

The boycott worked, and that night African Americans met to discuss whether to continue it. At the meeting, a newly arrived minister—Dr. Martin Luther King, Jr.—spoke and energized the crowd. The people decided to continue the boycott and named King as their leader. The boycott lasted more than a year. It ended when the Supreme Court ruled that the segregated city buses violated the rights of African Americans. With this success, King had begun his brilliant career as America's chief civil rights leader.

Life for Parks became difficult, however. She lost her job, and her husband was unable to work after suffering a nervous breakdown. They were plagued by threatening phone calls. Even after the boycott ended, no one would hire Parks. A year after the boycott ended, the Parkses moved to Detroit, where they had family. Rosa Parks made a living as a seamstress and also helped the local office of the Southern Christian Leadership Conference. In 1965 she joined the staff of a member of the U.S. House of Representatives from Detroit.

Over the years Parks has delivered speeches to raise money for the NAACP. In 1969 a street was named for her in Detroit. She has received many awards—most notably the 1984 Eleanor Roosevelt Women of Courage Award. In 1989 she attended the White House ceremony for the 25th anniversary of the Civil Rights Act, where she was acknowledged by President Bush.

Questions

1. Why is Parks called the "mother of the civil rights movement"?
2. Jo Ann Robinson recalled later that Parks was "dignified" and had "strong morals and high character." Why did that make her a good symbol to promote the bus boycott?
3. Explain in your own words what Parks's action meant to American history.

CHAPTER 21

Section 2

AMERICAN LIVES   A. Philip Randolph
A Life Fighting for Equality

"[African Americans] have reached the limit of their endurance when it comes to going into another Jim Crow Army to fight another war for democracy—a democracy they have never gotten."—A. Philip Randolph, testimony to the Senate Armed Services Committee, 1948

For many decades, A. Philip Randolph (1889–1979) worked to achieve equal rights for African Americans. His work began before World War I and did not end until the 1970s. His efforts had a profound effect on government policy.

Randolph was born and educated in Florida. After graduating from high school, he left home for New York City. He promised to return the next summer—but he never did. He took college courses that gave him a radical point of view. In 1917, he began a journal called *The Messenger*. He used it to denounce labor unions for refusing to aid African-American workers in their attempts to organize. He also campaigned against African Americans joining the army during World War I. Because of that stand, he was arrested, but he was soon released.

In the 1920s, Randolph continued speaking out. In 1925 he founded and became head of the Brotherhood of Sleeping Car Porters (BSCP). This union was formed by African Americans who worked as porters and maids on trains with sleeping cars. The Pullman Company, which employed them, refused to recognize the union. It fired workers who joined the union and threatened others not to join. Randolph tried to organize support for the union on the outside and spoke to inspire members. It took many years, but with the New Deal, the union had a chance. The Roosevelt administration passed laws that gave greater power to unions. In 1935, Pullman finally recognized the union. That same year Randolph won another victory. The American Federation of Labor (AFL) welcomed the Brotherhood as a member union. Two years later, Randolph and Pullman agreed to a new contract that raised workers' pay, cut their hours, and guaranteed money for overtime work.

Randolph's next major success came in 1941. In the early years of World War II, there was much debate about whether the United States should enter the war. Randolph loudly insisted that African Americans should not participate as long as racism continued at home. He organized the March on

Washington Movement and promised to lead thousands of blacks in a massive protest against the lack of equal rights. President Roosevelt feared that Nazi Germany would use such a protest for propaganda that would embarrass the United States. He tried to convince Randolph to call off the march, but Randolph refused. Finally, the president issued Executive Order 8802, stopping companies and unions that worked with the government from discriminating against blacks. He also set up the Fair Employment Practices Committee to investigate any cases of discrimination. Randolph then agreed to cancel the march.

A few years later, he put similar pressure on President Truman. Truman issued an order in 1948 to end segregation in the armed forces.

Throughout the 1950s, Randolph continued to work for African-American rights both within the labor movement and in the country at large. As the civil rights movement picked up steam in the 1950s and early 1960s, Randolph stepped forward. In 1963, he was named as the chief organizer of the massive march on Washington of August 28. He joined other leaders in meeting with President Kennedy to push him toward laws that would guarantee equal rights. The march helped create a climate of popular support that encouraged Congress to pass the Civil Rights Act of 1964 and Voting Rights Act of 1965. Randolph retired as head of the BSCP in 1968 but remained active in the civil rights movement until his death at age 90.

Questions

1. What did Randolph mean, in the quote at the top of the page, by a "Jim Crow Army"?
2. How did the New Deal help Randolph's fight on behalf of the Brotherhood?
3. Some African-American leaders criticized Randolph for canceling the 1941 march. Do you think he was right to do so? Explain.

Name _____ Date _____

GUIDED READING *Moving Toward Conflict*

A. As you read this section, take notes to answer questions about how the United
States slowly became involved in a war in Vietnam.

1941	Vietminh is formed. →	1. What did the Vietminh declare as its main goal?
1945	Japan is forced out of Vietnam. →	2. What did Ho Chi Minh declare after Japan was forced out?
1946	French troops return to southern Vietnam. →	3. How did Ho Chi Minh respond to the return of the French?

1950	U.S. begins its involvement in the Vietnam struggle. →	4. Whom did the U.S. support?	5. What aid did the U.S. provide?
		6. Why did the U.S. get involved in the struggle?	
1954	Eisenhower introduces domino theory. →	7. What did Eisenhower compare to a row of dominoes?	
	Vietminh over-runs Dien Bien Phu. →	8. What did this Vietminh victory cause the French to do?	
	Geneva Accords are reached. →	9. How did the Geneva Accords change Vietnam?	
1956	Elections are canceled. →	10. Who canceled the Vietnamese elections? Why?	
1957	Vietcong begins attacks on Diem government.		
1963	Diem is overthrown.	11. What authority did the Tonkin Gulf Resolution grant to the U.S. president?	
1964	U.S. Congress adopts Tonkin Gulf Resolution. →		
1965	Operation - Rolling Thunder is launched. →	12. What did Operation Rolling Thunder do in North Vietnam?	

B. On the back of this paper, explain the importance of the **Ho Chi Minh Trail** in
the Vietnam War.

Name _____ Date _____

GUIDED READING *U.S. Involvement and Escalation*

CHAPTER
22
Section 2

As you read about the escalation of the war, take notes to answer the questions.

1. What role did each of the following play in the decision to escalate U.S. military involvement in Vietnam?
Lyndon B. Johnson
Robert McNamara
Dean Rusk
William Westmoreland
U.S. Congress
American public opinion

U.S. military strategies result in a bloody stalemate.

2. What military advantages did the Americans have over the Vietcong?	3. What military advantages did the Vietcong have over the Americans?
4. What military strategies did the Americans use against the Vietcong?	5. What military strategies did the Vietcong use against the Americans?

Public support for the war begins to waver as a "credibility gap" grows.

6. What role did each of the following play in this change of public support?
The U.S. economy
Television
The Fulbright hearings

CHAPTER 22

Section 3

GUIDED READING *A Nation Divided*

As you read this section, take notes to answer the questions.

Avoiding the War
1. What were some of the ways that young American men avoided military service in Vietnam?
2. In what sense was the Vietnam War a "working-class" war? How did it become one?

Opposing the War
3. What organizations and groups of Americans tended to oppose the war?
4. What were some of the reasons that "doves" opposed the war?
5. In what ways did they show their opposition to the war?

Defending the War
6. By 1967, how did most Americans feel about U.S. involvement in the Vietnam War?
7. Why did "hawks" criticize the Johnson administration's policies in Vietnam?

© McDougal Littell Inc. All rights reserved.

CHAPTER
22
Section 4

GUIDED READING *1968: A Tumultuous Year*

A. As you read this section, note some of the causes and effects of the events of 1968. Leave the shaded box blank.

Causes	Events of 1968	Effects
	1. Tet Offensive	
	2. Johnson's poor showing in the New Hampshire primary	
	3. Assassination of Dr. Martin Luther King, Jr.	
	4. Assassination of Robert Kennedy	
	5. Disorder at the Democratic National Convention	
	6. Richard M. Nixon's presidential election victory	

B. On the back of this paper, note the political party of each of the following and describe the position that each held or sought in 1968: **Clark Clifford, Eugene McCarthy, Hubert Humphrey,** and **George Wallace.**

© McDougal Littell Inc. All rights reserved.

CHAPTER 22

Section 5

GUIDED READING *The End of the War and Its Legacy*

A. As you read about President Nixon's Vietnam policy and the end of the war, note one or more reasons for each of the following developments during the war.

1. Nixon adopts a policy of Vietnamization.	2. My Lai massacre shocks Americans.
3. Nixon orders invasion of Cambodia.	4. First student strike in U.S. history occurs.
5. Congress repeals the Tonkin Gulf Resolution.	6. The "Christmas bombings" take place.
7. South Vietnam surrenders to North Vietnam.	8. Vietnam veterans receive a cold homecoming.
9. Cambodia erupts in civil war.	10. Congress passes the War Powers Act.
11. The draft is abolished.	12. Many Americans lose faith in their government.

B. On the back of this paper, explain the significance of each of the following terms in relation to the Vietnam War:

silent majority   Pentagon Papers   Henry Kissinger   Khmer Rouge

Name _____ Date _____

CHAPTER 22 BUILDING VOCABULARY *The Vietnam War Years*

A. Multiple Choice Circle the letter before the term or name that best completes the sentence.

1. The Vietcong was the name given to the (a) North Vietnamese Army (b) Army of the Republic of Vietnam (c) Communist opposition group in South Vietnam.

2. The gasoline-based bomb used to destroy the dense jungles of Vietnam was called (a) napalm (b) Agent Orange (c) Mace.

3. The event that convinced many Americans that the war in Vietnam was unwinnable was the (a) My Lai massacre (b) Tet Offensive (c) Christmas bombings.

4. The leader of North Vietnam was (a) Ngo Dinh Diem (c) Nguyen Cao Ky (c) Ho Chi Minh.

5. The candidate who nearly upset President Lyndon Johnson in the New Hampshire Democratic primary in 1968 was (a) Eugene McCarthy (b) Robert Kennedy (c) Hubert Humphrey.

B. Completion Select the term or name that best completes the sentence.

domino theory	Free Speech Movement	War Powers Act
Henry Kissinger	Pentagon Papers	Geneva Accords
Dean Rusk	William Westmoreland	New Left

1. The _____, passed by Congress in the wake of Vietnam, sought to curb the president's war-making powers.

2. The American Commander in South Vietnam was _____.

3. The _____ described the belief that if Vietnam succumbed to communism, the other nations of Asia also would fall to the Communists.

4. The growing youth movement of the 1960s became known as the _____.

5. The _____ revealed that the government had been less than truthful to the American people about its Vietnam policies.

C. Writing Write a paragraph about the turmoil on the home front during the Vietnam War using the following terms.

hawk   **dove**   **credibility gap**

CHAPTER
22

Section 2

SKILLBUILDER PRACTICE *Distinguishing Fact from Opinion*

In his State of the Union Address of 1966, President Johnson spoke of the course of the war in Vietnam and U.S. efforts for peace there. Read the portion of his speech presented below. Then, beside each number at the bottom of the page, write "fact" if the underlined phrase with that number is a fact, or "opinion" if the phrase is an opinion. (See Skillbuilder Handbook, p. R9.)

[O]ur choice gradually became clear. We could leave, abandoning South Vietnam to its attackers and to certain conquest—or we could stay and fight beside the people of South Vietnam.

[1] We stayed, and we will stay until aggression has stopped.

We will stay there because [2] a just nation cannot leave to the cruelty of its enemies a people who have staked their lives and independence on America's solemn pledge, a pledge which has grown through the commitments of three American Presidents. . . .

We will stay because in Asia, and around the world, are countries whose independence rests in large measure on confidence in America's word and in America's protection.

To yield to force in Vietnam would weaken that confidence; would undermine the independence of many lands, and would whet the appetite of aggression. [3] We would have to fight in one land, and then we'd have to fight in another—or abandon much of Asia to the domination of the Communists. . . .

And we do not intend to abandon Asia to conquest.

[4] Last year, the nature of the war in Vietnam changed again. Swiftly increasing numbers of [5] armed men from the north crossed the borders to join forces that were already in the south; attack and terror increased, spurred and encouraged by the belief that [6] the United States lacked the will to continue and that their victory was near.

Despite our desire to limit conflict, [7] it was necessary to act to hold back the mounting aggression, to give courage to the people of the south, and to make our firmness clear to the north.

Thus, [8] we began limited air action against military targets in North Vietnam; [9] we increased our fighting force to its present strength tonight of 190,000 men.

These moves have not ended the aggression. But they have prevented its success. . . .

We seek neither territory nor bases, economic domination or military alliance in Vietnam. We fight for the principle of self-determination, that [10] the people of South Vietnam should be able to choose their own course—choose it in free elections, without violence, without terror and without fear.

1. _____

2. _____

3. _____

4. _____

5. _____

6. _____

7. _____

8. _____

9. _____

10. _____

RETEACHING ACTIVITY *Moving Toward Conflict*

Summarizing

A. Complete the chart below by explaining how each administration increased
America's involvement in Vietnam.

Administration	Action
Truman	
Eisenhower	
Kennedy	
Johnson	

Finding Main Ideas

B. Answer the following questions in the space provided.

1. What prompted the war between the Vietminh and the French?

_____

_____

2. What were the terms of the Geneva Accords?

_____

_____

3. What was the Tonkin Gulf Resolution?

_____

_____

CHAPTER 22

Section 2

RETEACHING ACTIVITY *U.S. Involvement and Escalation*

Finding Main Ideas

The following questions deal with America's entry into the Vietnam War. Answer them in the space provided.

1. How did most Americans react to President Johnson's decision to commit troops to the war in Vietnam? Why?

   _____

   _____

2. What difficulties did U.S. troops encounter in Vietnam?

   _____

   _____

3. What actions by U.S. troops hindered the effort to win the support of Vietnamese villagers?

   _____

   _____

4. What factors led to a decline in the morale of many U.S. soldiers?

   _____

   _____

5. How did the Vietnam War affect President Johnson's Great Society?

   _____

   _____

6. What role did television play in increasing Americans' doubts about the war effort?

   _____

   _____

CHAPTER
22
Section 3

RETEACHING ACTIVITY *A Nation Divided*

Matching

A. Match the description in the second column with the term or name in the first column. Write the appropriate letter next to the word.

_____ 1. hawk   a. led Free Speech Movement

_____ 2. college deferment   b. left Johnson administration to head World Bank

_____ 3. Tom Hayden   c. served in disproportionate numbers in Vietnam

_____ 4. dove   d. system that calls up citizens for military service

_____ 5. draft   e. founded Students for a Democratic Society

_____ 6. Mario Savio   f. favored stronger military force in Vietnam

_____ 7. African Americans   g. allowed students to put off military duty

_____ 8. Robert McNamara   h. advocated U.S. withdrawal from Vietnam

Evaluating

B. Write *T* in the blank if the statement is true. If the statement is false, write *F* in the blank and then write the corrected statement on the line below.

_____ 1. During the years of antiwar protest, no Americans fled the country in order to escape military service.

_____

_____ 2. The most common reason for opposition to the war was the belief that it was a civil conflict in which the United States had no business fighting.

_____

_____ 3. Women joined in the war effort by volunteering their services to relief and hospitality groups such as the American Red Cross and the United Services Organization.

_____

_____ 4. Martin Luther King, Jr. supported the war in Vietnam because it gave African Americans the chance to demonstrate their valor and patriotism.

_____

_____ 5. Many of the men who fought in Vietnam were from the ranks of America's upper-class white citizens.

_____

CHAPTER

22

Section 4

RETEACHING ACTIVITY *1968: A Tumultuous Year*

Sequencing

A. Put the events below in the correct chronological order.

_____ 1. President Johnson announces he will not seek a second term.

_____ 2. Robert Kennedy is assassinated.

_____ 3. The Tet Offensive shocks America.

_____ 4. Richard Nixon is elected as president.

_____ 5. President Johnson narrowly wins the New Hampshire primary.

_____ 6. Riots mar the Democratic National Convention in Chicago.

Completion

B. Select the term or name that best completes the sentence.

domino theory	Israel	Walter Cronkite
doves	Kent State	Yippies
law and order	Clark Clifford	Columbia University

1. After the Tet Offensive, the renowned journalist _____ declared that the Vietnam War seemed destined "to end in a stalemate."

2. Robert Kennedy was assassinated by a Palestinian immigrant who said he was angered by Kennedy's support of _____.

3. In April 1968, the students at _____ held a massive protest over the school's community policies.

4. Richard Nixon won support during the presidential race by vowing to restore _____ to the country.

5. The group of antiwar protesters who many believe had come to the Democratic National Convention to provoke violence and chaos were called the _____.

Name _____ Date _____

CHAPTER
22
Section 5

RETEACHING ACTIVITY *The End of the War and Its Legacy*

Multiple Choice

Choose the best answer for each item. Write the letter of your answer in the blank.

_____ 1. The event that in the spring of 1970 stirred a new round of antiwar protests was the
     a. My Lai massacre.
     b. invasion of Cambodia.
     c. release of the Pentagon Papers.
     d. Christmas bombings.

_____ 2. The Pentagon Papers were leaked by former Defense Department worker
     a. Henry Kissinger.
     b. H. R. Haldeman.
     c. William Calley, Jr.
     d. Daniel Ellsberg.

_____ 3. The number of Americans killed in Vietnam was roughly
     a. 10,000.
     b. 25,000.
     c. 58,000.
     d. 96,000.

_____ 4. After the United States withdrew from the Vietnam War, North and South Vietnam
     a. agreed to exist as separate nations.
     b. continued fighting until North Vietnam emerged victorious.
     c. continued fighting until South Vietnam emerged victorious.
     d. fought to a stalemate and signed a cease-fire that exists today.

_____ 5. In the wake of the Vietnam War, Cambodia fell to the brutal Communist regime known as the
     a. Khmer Rouge.
     b. Vietcong.
     c. Vietminh.
     d. Bolsheviks.

_____ 6. According the War Powers Act, Congress must give its consent for U.S. troops to remain in a hostile region any longer than
     a. 30 days.
     b. 90 days
     c. six months.
     d. one year.

CHAPTER 22

Section 4

GEOGRAPHY APPLICATION: LOCATION

The Ho Chi Minh Trail

Directions: Read the paragraphs below and study the map carefully. Then answer the questions that follow.

The Ho Chi Minh Trail developed from a network of existing hidden jungle paths. During the 1960s, it became the main route used by North Vietnam to get troops and supplies into South Vietnam in support of the Vietcong's fight against South Vietnamese troops and their U.S. allies. The trail was named for Ho Chi Minh, the leader of North Vietnam at the time. When North Vietnamese soldiers were wounded, they were transported up the trail for treatment.

U.S. and South Vietnamese troops tried repeatedly to cut or destroy this lifeline. They drenched the surrounding jungle with defoliants to kill trees and other vegetation. This effort failed, and North Vietnam continued to use the trail.

The Tet Offensive of early 1968 showed how determined North Vietnam was. The North Vietnamese and the Vietcong launched simultaneous raids on provincial capitals and major cities throughout South Vietnam at the beginning of Tet, the lunar new year celebration. The U.S. Embassy in Saigon was attacked, as were many other supposedly secure sites. The planning and coordination needed to carry out such an action stunned Americans in Vietnam and in the United States. The Tet Offensive, though not a North Vietnamese victory in the sense that it captured territory or inflicted great casualties, still caused many Americans to rethink their nation's involvement in the Vietnam War.

In 1971, South Vietnamese troops invaded Laos in an attempt to cut of the flow of men and supplies along the trail. Despite American air support, the invasion was a disaster, and the South Vietnamese army was defeated by North Vietnamese forces.

The Ho Chi Minh Trail, along which more than 20,000 troops a month could be moved by 1967, was the key to keeping North Vietnam in the war until the United States tired of battle and controversy and pulled out.

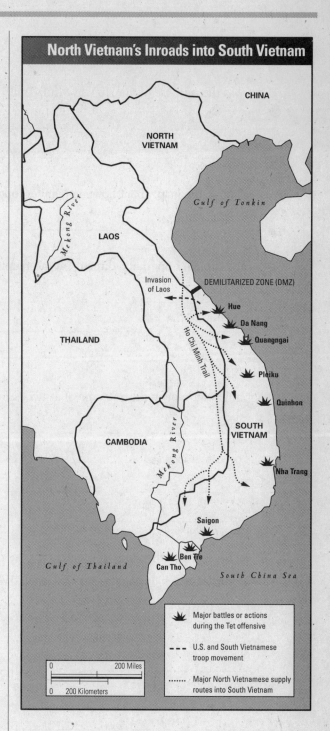

North Vietnam's Inroads into South Vietnam

Major battles or actions during the Tet offensive

- - - U.S. and South Vietnamese troop movement

.... Major North Vietnamese supply routes into South Vietnam

0 — 200 Miles

0 — 200 Kilometers

Interpreting Text and Visuals

1. Describe the path of the Ho Chi Minh Trail. _____

_____

_____

_____

2. What was the purpose of the Ho Chi Minh Trail? _____

_____

_____

3. According to the map, about how many miles long was the Ho Chi Minh Trail? _____

_____

4. Describe the 1971 operation directed at interrupting the Ho Chi Minh Trail. _____

_____

_____

_____

5. What might have been the outcome of a successful invasion of Laos in 1971? _____

_____

_____

_____

6. Reread the text and then look at the map for the northernmost and southern-
   most points of attack during the Tet Offensive. What part do you think the Ho Chi
   Minh Trail played in the attacks? _____

_____

_____

_____

_____

CHAPTER
22
Section 5

OUTLINE MAP *The Vietnam War*

A. Review the maps "Indochina, 1959" and "Tet Offensive, Jan. 30–Feb. 24, 1968" on pages 733 and 749 of your textbook. Then, on the accompanying outline map, label the following bodies of water, countries, and cities. Finally, draw a line to mark the DMZ, the Demilitarized Zone that separated North and South Vietnam.

Bodies of Water		Countries		Cities	
Gulf of Tonkin	Red River	South Vietnam	Thailand	Hanoi	Can Tho
South China Sea	Gulf of Thailand	North Vietnam	Laos	Hue	
Mekong River		Cambodia	China	Saigon	

B. After completing the map, use it to answer the following questions.

1. Which natural feature forms much of the border between Laos and Thailand?

_____

2. Why might the United States have been concerned early in the war about China's attitude toward U.S. involvement on the side of South Vietnam? _____

_____

_____

3. What city is located in the delta of the Red River? _____

   in the Mekong Delta area? _____

4. About how long was the DMZ that separated North from South Vietnam? _____

5. What might have been the effect on the Vietnam War if the border of Laos had been closed and North Vietnam had not been able to operate in the country? _____

_____

_____

_____

6. The Tet offensive ranged from Hue to Can Tho. Thus, over approximately how many miles did the North Vietnamese attacks stretch? _____

7. Part of the reason that the United States got involved in Vietnam was the domino theory—the belief in the 1950s and 1960s that the loss of even one country to communism would cause all others in the region to fall "like a row of dominoes." What countries is it likely that the United States feared losing to communism?

_____

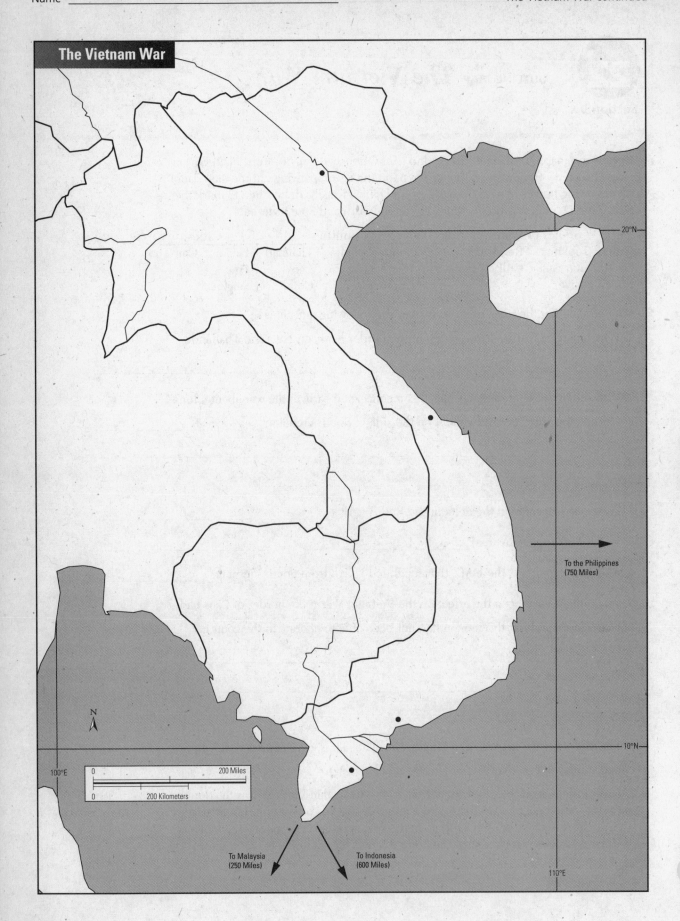

The Vietnam War

To the Philippines
(750 Miles)

To Malaysia
(250 Miles)

To Indonesia
(600 Miles)

100°E

110°E

20°N

10°N

N

0   200 Miles

0   200 Kilometers

Name _____   Date _____

PRIMARY SOURCE   Letter from a Soldier in Vietnam

Marine Second Lieutenant Marion Lee "Sandy" Kempner from Galveston, Texas, arrived in Vietnam in July 1966 and was killed four months later by shrapnel from a mine explosion near Tien Phu. He wrote the following letter to his great-aunt less than three weeks before his death at the age of 24.

October 20, 1966

Dear Aunt Fannie,

This morning, my platoon and I were finishing up a three-day patrol. Struggling over steep hills covered with hedgerows, trees, and generally impenetrable jungle, one of my men turned to me and pointed a hand, filled with cuts and scratches, at a rather distinguished-looking plant with soft red flowers waving gaily in the downpour (which had been going on ever since the patrol began) and said, "That is the first plant I have seen today which didn't have thorns on it." I immediately thought of you.

The plant, and the hill upon which it grew, was also representative of Vietnam. It is a country of thorns and cuts, of guns and marauding, of little hope and of great failure. Yet in the midst of it all, a beautiful thought, gesture, and even person can arise among it waving bravely at the death that pours down upon it. Some day this hill will be burned by napalm, and the red flower will crackle up and die among the thorns. So what was the use of it living and being a beauty among the beasts, if it must, in the end, die because of them, and with them? This is a question which is answered by Gertrude Stein's "A rose is a rose is a rose." You are what you are what you are. Whether you believe in God, fate, or the crumbling cookie, elements are so mixed in a being that make him what he is; his salvation from the thorns around him lies in the fact that he existed at all, in his very own personality. There was once a time when the Jewish idea of heaven and hell was the thoughts and opinions people had of you after you died. But what if the plant was on an isolated hill and was never seen by anyone? That is like the question of whether the falling tree makes a sound in the forest primeval when no one is there to hear it. It makes a sound, and the plant was beautiful and the thought was kind, and the person was humane, and distinguished and brave, not merely because other people recognized it as such, but because it is, and it is, and it is.

The flower will always live in the memory of a tired, wet Marine, and has thus achieved a sort of immortality. But even if we had never gone on that hill, it would still be a distinguished, soft, red, thornless flower growing among the cutting, scratching plants, and that in itself is its own reward.

Love,
Sandy

from Bernard Edelman, ed., *Dear America: Letters Home from Vietnam* (New York: Norton, 1985), 137–138.

Discussion Questions

1. In this letter, Lieutenant Kempner describes a plant. What does the plant look like?
2. What does this plant represent to Kempner?

3. Based on your reading of this letter, what qualities or traits do you think might have helped Kempner cope with the trials of war in Vietnam?

CHAPTER 22

Section 3

PRIMARY SOURCE Protest Buttons

These protest buttons from the antiwar movement in the 1960s were worn by Americans who opposed the war in Vietnam. What different views do the images and slogans on these buttons express?

Photos by Sharon Hoogstraten
Out Now Button: Archive Photos/Blank Archives

Activity Options

1. With a small group of classmates, discuss the slogans and symbols used in these buttons. Then choose two buttons that you think are most effective and explain your choices to the class.

2. Design your own protest button to express your view on the war in Vietnam, on war in general, or on a more recent controversial issue. Borrow symbols and slogans from those depicted on this page or invent your own.

CHAPTER

22

Section 3

PRIMARY SOURCE *The New Left*

Active in the New Left from the time of the Cuban missile crisis through the end of U.S. involvement in the Vietnam War, Dick Cluster was a member of the Harvard-Radcliffe chapter of Students for a Democratic Society (SDS). As you read this excerpt from Cluster's essay about student protest, consider his views on being part of the New Left.

An early memory . . . is the first national demonstration against the war—the SDS April 17, 1965, March on Washington to End the War in Vietnam. The speakers stormed and droned on for too long, the White House sat behind us apparently deaf. But there below the Washington Monument were more people than I had ever seen together except at baseball games.

Then someone at a microphone repeated a couple of times, "If Judy Collins or Joan Baez is in the crowd, could you please come to the microphone." In 1965, folk music was In, and these were Big Stars; I took the announcement for a joke. But sure enough, Joan Baez came to the microphone and as she sang "We Shall Overcome," 25,000 of us moved down the Mall to the Capitol, through the line of police who ordered us to stop. The only thing I could think was, "This is a Movement!"

The choice which that movement presented was: "Okay, be out there isolated, competing for things you don't want; or be in here, making history, here with us."

We were not afraid to experiment, and we were making something new. For myself, writing leaflets and newspapers, one thing that was particularly important was making a new vocabulary and (though we didn't call it that) a new ideology. But for most of us, I think, this new language was a part of what made us feel powerful and useful, not isolated and worthless.

"Participatory democracy" said what we felt we were lacking—participation in and control over what was happening to us. "The war machine" summed up both our political enemy and our feeling about what was wrong with the culture. "Corporate liberalism"— our attempt to define the outlook of the Johnson administration—spoke to our confusion about both *who* ran the country and to what end. Even a tactical gem like "the streets belong to the people" (chanted when we defied police orders to stick to planned march routes, or to disperse) compressed a lot into itself: a breakthrough into disruptive action as well as a growing awareness that our goal was to put the products the people sweat and pay for into the hands of the people.

All this language grew out of our trying to understand what we had done and what we were up against. That's why it spoke to so many people facing the same dilemmas, the same questions about the possibility of accomplishing any change.

Proof that we were really reaching people, really building something, was the Movement's growth. All around us we saw people joining and changing. Young people looked to us to tell them about themselves and their society. Suddenly we found a demand for radical "products." Radical courses flourished on campuses, radical newspapers off-campus.

So the Movement offered meaning and purpose, in a society that offered very little of either. Just as important, it offered community. . . .

I'm not saying that getting into a community like the *Old Mole* [a radical newspaper] collective was an easy task. The New Left was often cliquish. "There is no Movement outside our friends' living rooms," was a frequent self-criticism. Joining the Movement often meant feeling pulled away from old friends but unable to break into an inner circle of long-time activists.

But in comparison to mainstream America, the Movement offered a pretty good shot at a meaningful community. If you weren't as in as you wanted to be, still you felt a lot closer to what you were looking for. And the Movement, though cliquish, had a significant ability to inspire by example.

from Dick Cluster, ed., *They Should Have Served That Cup of Coffee: 7 Radicals Remember the 60s* (Boston: South End Press, 1979), 117–120.

Discussion Questions

1. According to Cluster, what were some of the advantages of being involved in the New Left?
2. In Cluster's opinion, what were some of the disadvantages of the New Left?
3. Why do you think many young people in the 1960s were drawn to the New Left?

CHAPTER 22 Section 4

PRIMARY SOURCE

Lyndon B. Johnson on Vietnam and Reelection

In a televised address to the nation on March 31, 1968, President Johnson outlined changes in Vietnam policy and concluded with the surprise announcement that he would not run for reelection. As you read part of Johnson's speech, consider what he offered to North Vietnam and why he decided not to seek the Democratic nomination.

Tonight I want to speak to you on peace in Vietnam and Southeast Asia.

No other question so preoccupies our people. No other dream so absorbs the 250 million human beings who live in that part of the world. No other goal motivates American policy in Southeast Asia.

For years, representatives of our government and others have traveled the world—seeking to find a basis for peace talks. Since last September, they have carried the offer I made public at San Antonio.

It was this: that the United States would stop its bombardment of North Vietnam when that would lead promptly to productive discussions—and that we would assume that North Vietnam would not take military advantage of our restraint. . . .

Tonight, I renew the offer I made last August—to stop the bombardment of North Vietnam. We ask that talks begin promptly and that they be serious talks on the substance of peace. We assume that during those talks Hanoi would not take advantage of our restraint. We are prepared to move immediately toward peace through negotiations.

Tonight, in the hope that this action will lead to early talks, I am taking the first step to deescalate the conflict. We are reducing—substantially reducing—the present level of hostilities. And we are doing so unilaterally, and at once.

Tonight, I have ordered our aircraft and naval vessels to make no attacks on North Vietnam, except in the area north of the Demilitarized Zone (DMZ) where the continuing enemy build-up directly threatens allied forward positions and where movements of troops and supplies are clearly related to that threat. . . .

I call upon President Ho Chi Minh to respond positively and favorably to this new step toward peace.

But if peace does not come now through negotiations, it will come when Hanoi understands that our common resolve is unshakable and our common strength is invincible. . . .

In these times, as in times before, it is true that a house divided against itself—by the spirit of faction, of party, of region, of religion, of race—is a house that cannot stand. There is divisiveness in the American house now. . . .

What we won when all our people united must not now be lost in suspicion, distrust, and selfishness or politics among any of our people.

Believing this as I do, I have concluded that I should not permit the presidency to become involved in the partisan divisions that are developing in this political year. With America's sons in the field far away, with America's future under challenge here at home, with our hopes and the world's hopes for peace in the balance every day, I do not believe that I should devote an hour or a day of my time to any duties other than the awesome duties of this office, the presidency of your country.

Accordingly, I shall not seek and I will not accept the nomination of my party for another term as your President. But, let men everywhere know, however, that a strong and confident, a vigilant America stands ready to seek an honorable peace and stands ready to defend an honored cause, whatever the price, whatever the burden, whatever the sacrifice that duty may require.

Thank you for listening. Goodnight, and God bless all of you.

from *Chicago Sun-Times*, April 1, 1968. Reprinted in Encyclopaedia Britannica, *1961–1968: The Burdens of World Power*, vol. 18 of *The Annals of America* (Chicago: Encyclopaedia Britannica, 1968), 613–616.

Discussion Questions

1. What offer did President Johnson make to North Vietnam?
2. Why did he decide not to seek the Democratic nomination for president?
3. How do you think antiwar activists responded to Johnson's speech?

LITERATURE SELECTION *from* **In Country**
by Bobbie Ann Mason

In the summer of 1984, Sam Hughes wants to learn more about her father who was killed in Vietnam before she was born. In this excerpt, Sam, her grandmother, and her uncle Emmett—himself a Vietnam veteran—make a pilgrimage to Washington, D.C., where they visit the Vietnam Veterans Memorial.

Emmett holds Mamaw's arm protectively and steers her across the street. The pot of geraniums hugs his chest.

"There it is," Sam says.

It is massive, a black gash in a hillside, like a vein of coal exposed and then polished with polyurethane. A crowd is filing by slowly, staring at it solemnly.

"Law," says Sam's grandmother quietly. "It's black as night."

"Here's the directory," Emmett says, pausing at the entrance. "I'll look up his name for you, Mrs. Hughes."

The directory is on a pedestal with a protective plastic shield. Sam stands in the shade, looking forward, at the black wing embedded in the soil, with grass growing above. It is like a giant grave, fifty-eight thousand bodies rotting here behind those names. The people are streaming past, down into the pit.

"It don't show up good," Mamaw says anxiously. "It's just a hole in the ground."

The memorial cuts a V in the ground, like the wings of an abstract bird, huge and headless. Overhead, a jet plane angles upward, taking off.

"It's on Panel 9E," Emmett reports. "That's on the east wing. We're on the west."

At the bottom of the wall is a granite trough, and on the edge of it the sunlight reflects the names just above, in mirror writing, upside down. Flower arrangements are scattered at the base. A little kid says, "Look, Daddy, the flowers are dying." The man snaps, "Some are and some aren't."

The walkway is separated from the memorial by a strip of gravel, and on the other side of the walk is a border of dark gray brick. The shiny surface of the wall reflects the Lincoln Memorial and the Washington Monument, at opposite angles.

A woman in a sunhat is focusing a camera on the wall. She says to the woman with her, "I didn't think it would look like this. Things aren't what you think they look like. I didn't know it was a wall."

A spraddle-legged guy in camouflage clothing walks by with a cane. Probably he has an artificial leg, Sam thinks, but he walks along proudly, as if he has been here many times before and doesn't have any particular business at that moment. He seems to belong here, like Emmett hanging out at McDonald's.

A group of schoolkids tumble through, noisy as chickens. As they enter, one of the girls says, "Are they piled on top of each other?" They walk a few steps farther and she says, "What are all these names anyway?" Sam feels like punching the girl in the face for being so dumb. How could anybody that age not know? But she realizes that she doesn't know either. She is just beginning to understand. And she will never really know what happened to all these men in the war. Some people walk by, talking as though they are on a Sunday picnic, but most are reverent, and some of them are crying.

Sam stands in the center of the V, deep in the pit. The V is like the white wings of the shopping mall in Paducah. The Washington Monument is reflected at the center line. If she moves slightly to the left, she sees the monument, and if she moves the other way she sees a reflection of the flag opposite the memorial. Both the monument and the flag seem like arrogant gestures, like the country giving the finger to the dead boys, flung in this hole in the ground. Sam doesn't understand what she is feeling, but it is something so strong, it is like a tornado moving in her, something massive and overpowering. It feels like giving birth to this wall.

"I wish Tom could be here," Sam says to Emmett. "He needs to be here." Her voice is thin, like smoke, barely audible.

"He'll make it here someday. Jim's coming too. They're all coming one of these days."

"Are you going to look for anybody's name besides my daddy's?"

"Yeah."

"Who?"

"Those guys I told you about, the ones that died

all around me that day. And that guy I was going to look up—he might be here. I don't know if he made it out or not."

Sam gets a flash of Emmett's suffering, his grieving all these years. He has been grieving for fourteen years. In this dazzling sunlight, his pimples don't show. A jet plane flies overhead, close to the earth. Its wings are angled back too, like a bird's.

Two workmen in hard hats are there with a stepladder and some loud machinery. One of the workmen, whose hat says on the back NEVER AGAIN, seems to be drilling into the wall.

"What's he doing, hon?" Sam hears Mamaw say behind her.

"It looks like they're patching up a hole or something." *Fixing a hole where the rain gets in.*

The man on the ladder turns off the tool, a sander, and the other workman hands him a brush. He brushes the spot. Silver duct tape is patched around several names, leaving the names exposed. The names are highlighted in yellow, as though someone has taken a Magic Marker and colored them, the way Sam used to mark names and dates, important facts, in her textbooks.

"Somebody must have vandalized it," says a man behind Sam. "Can you imagine the sicko who would do that?"

"No," says the woman with him. "Somebody just wanted the names to stand out and be noticed. I can go with that."

"Do you think they colored Dwayne's name?" Mamaw asks Sam worriedly.

"No. Why would they?" Sam gazes at the flowers spaced along the base of the memorial. A white carnation is stuck in a crack between two panels of the wall. A woman bends down and straightens a ribbon on a wreath. The ribbon has gold letters on it, "VFW Post 7215 of Pa."

They are moving slowly. Panel 9E is some distance ahead. Sam reads a small poster propped at the base of the wall: "To those men of C Company, 1st Bn. 503 Inf., 173rd Airborne who were lost in the battle for Hill 823, Dak To, Nov. 11, 1967. Because of their bravery I am here today. A grateful buddy."

A man rolls past in a wheelchair. Another jet plane flies over.

A handwritten note taped to the wall apologizes to one of the names for abandoning him in a firefight.

Mamaw turns to fuss over the geraniums in Emmett's arms, the way she might fluff a pillow.

The workmen are cleaning the yellow paint from the names. They sand the wall and brush it carefully, like men polishing their cars. The man on the ladder sprays water on the name he has just sanded and wipes it with a rag.

Sam, conscious of how slowly they are moving, with dread, watches two uniformed marines searching and searching for a name. "He must have been along here somewhere," one says. They keep looking, running their hands over the names.

"There it is. That's him."

They read his name and both look abruptly away, stare out for a moment in the direction of the Lincoln Memorial, then walk briskly off.

"May I help you find someone's name?" asks a woman in a T-shirt and green pants. She is a park guide, with a clipboard in her hand.

"We know where we are," Emmett says. "Much obliged, though."

At panel 9E, Sam stands back while Emmett and Mamaw search for her father's name. Emmett, his gaze steady and intent, faces the wall, as though he were watching birds; and Mamaw, through her glasses, seems intent and purposeful, as though she were looking for something back in the field, watching to see if a cow had gotten out of the pasture. Sam imagines the egret patrolling for ticks on a water buffalo's back, ducking and snaking its head forward, its beak like a punji stick.

"There it is," Emmet says. It is far above his head, near the top of the wall. He reaches up and touches the name. "There's his name, Dwayne E. Hughes."

"I can't reach it," says Mamaw. "Oh, I wanted to touch it," she says softly, in disappointment.

"We'll set the flowers here, Mrs. Hughes," says Emmett. He sets the pot at the base of the panel, tenderly, as though tucking in a baby.

"I'm going to bawl," Mamaw says, bowing her head and starting to sob. "I wish I could touch it."

Sam has an idea. She sprints over to the workmen and asks them to let her borrow the stepladder. They are almost finished, and they agree. One of them brings it over and sets it up beside the wall, and Sam urges Mamaw to climb the ladder, but Mamaw protests. "No, I can't do it. You do it."

"Go ahead, ma'am," the workman says.

"Emmett and me'll hold the ladder," says Sam.

"Somebody might see up my dress."

"No, go on, Mrs. Hughes. You can do it," says Emmett. "Come on, we'll help you reach it."

He takes her arm. Together, he and Sam steady her while she places her foot on the first step and swings herself up. She seems scared, and she doesn't speak. She reaches but cannot touch the name.

"One more, Mamaw," says Sam, looking up at her grandmother—at the sagging wrinkles, her flab hanging loose and sad, and her eyes reddened with crying. Mamaw reaches toward the name and slowly struggles up the next step, holding her dress tight against her. She touches the name, running her hand over it, stroking it tentatively, affectionately, like feeling a cat's back. Her chin wobbles, and after a moment she backs down the ladder silently.

When Mamaw is down, Sam starts up the ladder, with the record package in her hand.

"Here, take the camera, Sam. Get his name." Mamaw has brought Donna's Instamatic.

"No, I can't take a picture this close."

Sam climbs the ladder until she is eye level with her father's name. She feels funny, touching it. A scratching on a rock. Writing. Something for future archaeologists to puzzle over, clues to a language.

"Look this way, Sam," Mamaw says. "I want to take your picture. I want to get you and his name and the flowers in together if I can."

"The name won't show up," Sam says.

"Smile."

"How can I smile?" She is crying.

Mamaw backs up and snaps two pictures. Sam feels her face looking blank. Up on the ladder, she feels so tall, like a spindly weed that is sprouting up out of this diamond-bright seam of hard earth. She sees Emmett at the directory, probably searching for his buddies' names. She touches her father's name again.

"All I can see here is my reflection," Mamaw says when Sam comes down the ladder. "I hope his name shows up. And your face was all shadow."

"Wait here a minute," Sam says, turning away her tears from Mamaw. She hurries to the directory on the east side. Emmett isn't there anymore. She sees him striding along the wall, looking for a certain panel. Nearby, a group of marines is keeping a vigil for the POWs and MIAs. A double row of flags is planted in the dirt alongside their table. One of the marines walks by with a poster: "You Are an American, Your Voice Can Make the Difference." Sam flips through the directory and finds "Hughes." She wants to see her father's name there too. She runs down the row of Hughes names. There were so many Hughes boys killed, names she doesn't know. His name is there, and she gazes at it for a moment. Then suddenly her own name leaps out at her.

SAM ALAN HUGHES PFC AR 02 MAR 49 O2 FEB 67 HOUSTON TX 14E 104

Her heart pounding, she rushes to panel 14E, and after racing her eyes over the string of names for a moment, she locates her own name.

SAM A HUGHES. It is the first on a line. It is down low enough to touch. She touches her own name. How odd it feels, as though all the names in America have been used to decorate this wall.

Mamaw is there at her side, clutching at Sam's arm, digging in with her fingernails. Mamaw says, "Coming up on this wall of a sudden and seeing how black it was, it was so awful, but then I came down in it and saw that white carnation blooming out of that crack and it gave me hope. It made me know he's watching over us." She loosens her bird-claw grip. "Did we lose Emmett?"

Silently, Sam points to the place where Emmett is studying the names low on a panel. He is sitting there cross-legged in front of the wall, and slowly his face bursts into a smile like flames.

Research Option

Find out the dimensions of the Vietnam Veterans Memorial, how many visitors come visit it annually, and other facts about the memorial.

CHAPTER
22
Section 2

AMERICAN LIVES Robert McNamara
The Legacy of Vietnam

"Looking back, I clearly erred by not forcing . . . a knock-down, drag-out debate over the loose assumptions, unasked questions, and thin analyses underlying our military strategy in Vietnam."—Robert McNamara, **In Retrospect (1995)**

Robert McNamara made the U.S. Defense Department more organized and efficient. Later he led an aid agency that funded programs to help poor people around the world improve their lives. However, he will probably be remembered most for his role in the Vietnam War.

McNamara (b. 1916) graduated from college with honors and attended the famous Harvard Business School. During World War II, he trained officers in the Army Air Corps in management techniques. After the war, he and a team of other managers joined the Ford Motor Company. These "Whiz Kids" led Ford out of difficulty and into new success. McNamara was named president of Ford—the first to come from outside the family. In 1961 he left that post to become President Kennedy's secretary of defense.

McNamara reformed the Defense Department and tightened control of the armed services. He joined in the planning that helped resolve the Cuban Missile Crisis. He also won Kennedy's approval of the new doctrine of "flexible response." This idea reduced the nation's heavy reliance on nuclear weapons. Instead, it based U.S. security on large conventional troop forces that could respond quickly to international crises.

The central issue of McNamara's time in office, though, was the Vietnam War. McNamara visited Vietnam in 1962, talking to leaders and American officers there. He backed the idea of using American troops as advisors and believed that with American help, the war could be over by 1965. After Kennedy was assassinated, he stayed as defense secretary under Lyndon Johnson, who came to rely on McNamara greatly.

McNamara supported the Gulf of Tonkin Resolution, which gave Johnson sweeping power in Vietnam. When administration planners debated whether to start bombing North Vietnam, McNamara thought it would not work, but he went along with the decision. He agreed with the policy of sending more troops.

As time went on, though, McNamara grew to believe that the Vietnam War could not be won. In meetings with Johnson and other top advisors, he expressed these doubts. In public, however, McNamara never voiced these concerns.

He became so identified with Vietnam policy that war critics often attacked him personally. They called the fight "McNamara's war" and branded him a "baby burner" for air attacks that resulted in the deaths of children. McNamara persuaded Johnson to halt the bombing at the end of 1965, hoping for a peaceful gesture in return from the other side. There was no response. In 1966, a McNamara peace proposal was secretly sent to North Vietnam. Again, there was no response.

In 1968, McNamara felt he could not continue in the administration. He left the Defense Department to become president of an international aid agency. He served as chief of the World Bank for fifteen years. Before him, that agency concentrated on funding large industrial projects around the world. McNamara shifted the focus. Under him, the bank concentrated on funding programs that worked to help the poorest people in the world more directly.

In 1995, McNamara published his memoirs—*In Retrospect: The Tragedy and Lessons of Vietnam.* The book revealed his earlier doubts that the war could be won. He said loyalty to Johnson prevented him from saying anything, even after he left office. Many reviewers criticized him for remaining quiet for so long and not having the courage of his convictions and speaking out at the time of the war.

Questions

1. Would you say that McNamara was effective at leading organizations? Why or why not?
2. Why did McNamara come to believe that fighting the Vietnam War was a mistake?
3. Do you agree that McNamara should have spoken out against the war when he left the Defense Department?

CHAPTER
22
Section 4

AMERICAN LIVES ## John Lewis
Moral Force for Nonviolence

"We got arrested for the first time and I felt good about it. We felt we were involved in a crusade and, in order to do something about it, you had to put your body on the line. We felt we could bring about change in the South."
—John Lewis, recalling his feelings after joining in his first sit-in, 1973

John Lewis (b. 1940) has worked outside the system in the civil rights movement. He has worked inside the system as the head of a federal agency and as a member of the U.S. House of Representatives. Wherever he has worked, Lewis has urged the nonviolent pursuit of equal rights.

Lewis was born to an Alabama farm family. He hoped to become a minister one day and listened on the radio to the speeches and sermons of Dr. Martin Luther King, Jr., who became his model. At college in Nashville, Tennessee, he joined workshops to learn the principles of nonviolent protest. These principles appealed to his deep faith.

In 1960, Lewis and other students heard about successful sit-ins being staged in North Carolina. They decided to stage similar protests. Over the next few weeks, they were arrested many times for breaking the city's segregation laws. That spring, Lewis and other students from across the South organized the Student Nonviolent Coordinating Committee (SNCC).

In 1961, Lewis joined in the freedom rides. In the beatings that took place in Montgomery, Alabama, Lewis was knocked unconscious. Nevertheless, he continued with the freedom rides throughout the summer. That fall the Interstate Commerce Commission ruled that segregation was illegal on interstate buses.

In 1963, Lewis was voted chairman of SNCC. He left school to devote himself full time to the movement. In the 1963 march on Washington, the young Lewis joined veteran civil rights leaders King and Roy Wilkins of the National Association for the Advancement of Colored People (NAACP) as one of the principal sponsors and speakers. The next year, he organized the voter registration drive called Mississippi Freedom Summer. In 1965, Lewis and King organized the march from Montgomery to Selma, Alabama. In the clubbings that took place on the Edmund Pettus Bridge, Lewis's skull was fractured. He recovered enough to help lead the second march two weeks later.

Lewis was feeling increasing frustration. He was tired of being beaten, and the growing war in Vietnam disturbed him. An advocate of nonviolence, he was a conscientious objector—someone who opposed all war on principle. An opponent of racism, he urged African Americans to resist the draft until they had won equal rights.

During this time, Lewis continued to serve as chairman of SNCC. However, many members now wanted a more radical approach to the struggle for rights. In 1966, one of these radicals was elected chairman, defeating Lewis. A few months later, Lewis resigned from the organization he had helped found and had led for three years.

In the next few years, Lewis continued his civil rights work in various organizations. Most noteworthy was his work in a project that helped register a million new African-American voters. In 1978, President Carter named him to head ACTION. This agency had responsibility for such volunteer programs as the Peace Corps and Vista. Lewis changed policy to put the agencies in closer touch with community groups.

In 1986, Lewis won election to the House of Representatives from Georgia. He has been reelected every two years since then, winning his sixth term in 1996. House colleagues have given him great respect due to the sacrifices he made in the civil rights movement and his principled stands on current issues.

Questions
1. How was Lewis's commitment to nonviolence tested in his life?
2. Lewis said he left SNCC when radicals took control because "violence . . . might deliver some quick solutions, but in the long run it debases you." What did he mean?
3. In 1991, Lewis opposed the use of force against Iraq. How is this stand—even if it was unpopular—not surprising?

Name _____ Date _____

CHAPTER
23
Section 1

GUIDED READING *Latinos and Native Americans*
Seek Equality

As you read, fill in the chart with answers to the questions.

What did Latinos campaign for?	How did some Latino individuals and groups go about getting what they wanted?	What federal laws (if any) were passed to address these needs?
1. Improved working conditions and better treatment for farm workers		
2. Educational programs for Spanish-speaking students		
3. More political power		

What did Native Americans campaign for?	How did some Native American individuals and groups go about getting what they wanted?	What federal laws (if any) were passed to address these needs?
4. Healthier, more secure lives of their own choosing		
5. Restoration of Indian lands, burial grounds, fishing and timber rights		

Name _____ Date _____

GUIDED READING *Women Fight for Equality*

CHAPTER
23
Section 2

A. As you read about the rise of a new women's movement, take notes to explain how each of the following helped to create or advance the movement.

1. Experiences in the workplace	2. Experiences in social activism
3. "Consciousness raising"	4. Feminism
5. Betty Friedan and *The Feminine Mystique*	6. Civil Rights Act of 1964
7. National Organization for Women (NOW)	8. Gloria Steinem and *Ms.* magazine
9. Congress	10. Supreme Court

B. The Equal Rights Amendment would have guaranteed equal rights under the law, regardless of gender. Who opposed this amendment? Why?

1. Who?	2. Why?

Name _____ Date _____

GUIDED READING *Culture and Counterculture*

As you read this section, fill out the chart below by listing and describing various elements of the counterculture of the 1960s.

1. Members or participants	2. Beliefs about American society	3. Goals for society and for themselves
4. Movement center	5. Attitudes and activities	6. Violent episodes
7. Impact on art and fashion	8. Impact on music	9. Impact on mainstream America

Name _____ Date _____

BUILDING VOCABULARY *An Era of Social Change*

A. Matching Match the description in the second column with name or term in the first column. Write the appropriate letter next to the word.

_____ 1. Betty Friedan a. fought to improve conditions for farm workers

_____ 2. American Indian Movement b. coalition of anti-feminist forces

_____ 3. New Right c. belief in equal rights for men and women

_____ 4. counterculture d. author of *The Feminine Mystique*

_____ 5. César Chávez e. militant Native American rights group

_____ 6. feminsim f. group that abandoned mainstream America

B. Multiple Choice Circle the letter before the term or name that best completes the sentence.

1. The unofficial capital of the counterculture movement was (a) New York City (b) Haight-Ashbury (c) Woodstock.

2. A prominent leader of the effort to defeat the Equal Rights Amendment (a) Phyllis Schlafly (b) Gloria Stienam (c) Betty Friedan.

3. In 1970, Texan José Angel Gutierrez established the political force known as (a) United Farm Workers Organizing Committee (UFWOC) (b) Alianza Federal de Mercedes (Federal Alliance of Land Grants) (c) La Raza Unida (the United People party).

4. The group whose quest for land rights, better living conditions, and more cultural respect often led to clashes with the government was (a) the American Indian Movement (AIM) (b) the National Organization of Women (NOW) (c) the counterculture.

CHAPTER 23

Section 3

SKILLBUILDER PRACTICE *Comparing; Contrasting*

Although decades apart, the hippies of the 1960s and the flappers of the 1920s both reflected youthful rebellion. In what other ways were these two movements similar? How were they different? Read the passage below, then fill in the Venn diagram to compare and contrast these two groups. (See Skillbuilder Handbook, p. R8.)

Countercultures The flappers of the 1920s and the hippies of the 1960s both belonged to movements against the values and, in many cases, strict social rules of the established "adult" society of their times.

In the 1920s, that conventional society may have seemed rather staid and stuffy to young people caught up in the Jazz Age. Those young men and women reflected a new sense of freedom, fun, and a kind of easy self-confidence. Relationships between women and men became much freer than in the past. Unlike their parents, these "flaming youth" went on dates without chaperones. They played with bold enthusiasm, driving recklessly and partying wildly to the strains of exciting new jazz.

Even the styles of women's fashion changed. Instead of heavy, long skirts and tight corsets of the previous generation, young women chose short, straight dresses. Flappers wore their hair cut short and close to the head. They also used bright lipstick and cheek color, which had not been acceptable in "polite society" up until then. Some of their elders looked on these young people as immoral.

Youthful Idealism By the 1960s, young people began protesting against the materialistic and militaristic emphasis they saw in their parents' generation. Many hippies seeking a different way of life joined together to form communes, where they lived and worked together. They believed in open, free relationships between men and women. Hippies also turned to new forms of rock 'n' roll as ways to express themselves. Many people with more conventional views saw the hippies' music and lifestyle as indecent and threatening to society.

As a reaction to what they saw as artificial, "establishment" fashions, young women turned away from the more conventional short skirts, dramatic make-up, and stiff, structured hair styles of their times, choosing instead worn jeans or long, flowing dresses, the natural look of no make-up, and soft, loose hair.

Not all young people in the '60s or the '20s rebelled against conventional culture. However, both groups were highly visible representations of changes that were taking place throughout the United States.

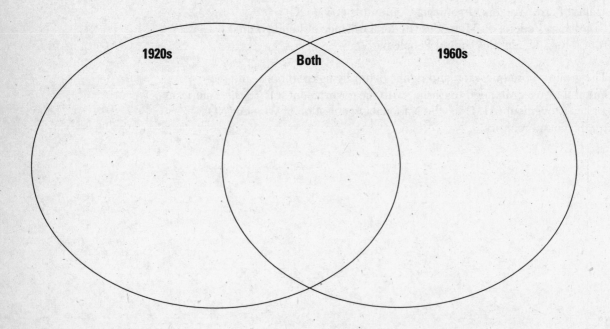

Name _____   Date _____

CHAPTER
23
SECTION 1

RETEACHING ACTIVITY *Latinos and Native Americans*
Seek Equality

Multiple Choice

Choose the best answer for each item. Write the letter of your answer in the blank.

_____ 1. During the 1960s, the Latino population in the United States grew to about
   a. 3 million.
   b. 6 million.
   c. 9 million.
   d. 12 million.

_____ 2. The largest Latino group in the United States is represented by people with ties to
   a. Mexico.
   b. Cuba.
   c. Puerto Rico.
   d. Central America.

_____ 3. During the late 1960s, César Chávez led a boycott against
   a. auto makers.
   b. grape growers.
   c. restaurant owners.
   d. clothing manufacturers.

_____ 4. Russell Means was a leader of
   a. La Raza Unida.
   b. the Brown Berets.
   c. the American Indian Movement.
   d. the National Council on Indian Opportunity.

_____ 5. César Chávez's strategy for improving work conditions for farm laborers was to
   a. organize a sit-down strike.
   b. improve public education.
   c. elect more supportive politicians.
   d. form a union.

_____ 6. Throughout the 1970s and 1980s, Native Americans won various victories in court
   granting them
   a. voting rights.
   b. land rights.
   c. better housing.
   d. equal employment opportunities.

Name _____ Date _____

RETEACHING ACTIVITY *Women Fight for Equality*

Summarizing

A. Complete the graphic below by highlighting the significant gains and setbacks of the women's movement of the 1960s and 1970s.

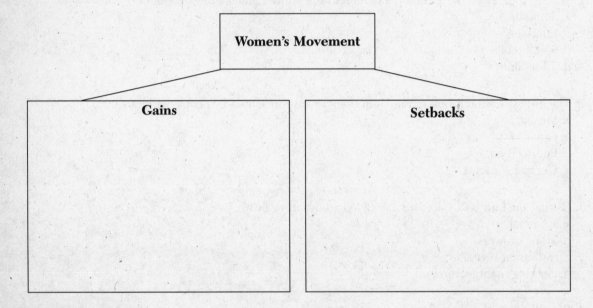

Finding Main Ideas

B. Answer the following questions in the space provided.

1. What was the message of *The Feminine Mystique*? What was the book's significance?

_____

_____

2. What role did the civil rights and antiwar movements play in the rise of the women's movement?

_____

_____

3. Why did some women, including Phyllis Schlafly, oppose the Equal Rights Amendment?

_____

_____

CHAPTER
23
SECTION 3

RETEACHING ACTIVITY *Culture and Counterculture*

Finding Main Ideas

The following questions deal with the counterculture movement. Answer them in the space provided.

1. What beliefs did the members of the counterculture share with the larger youth movement?

_____

_____

2. What was the goal of the counterculture movement?

_____

_____

3. What were the main characteristics of the hippie movement?

_____

_____

4. What led to the decline of the counterculture movement?

_____

_____

5. In what ways did aspects of the counterculture impact mainstream society?

_____

_____

6. What was the response of conservatives to the counterculture?

_____

_____

GEOGRAPHY APPLICATION: REGION

CHAPTER 23

Section 2

The Equal Rights Amendment

***Directions: Read the paragraphs below and study the map carefully. Then answer
the questions that follow.***

In 1970 the Equal Rights Amendment (ERA), which had been introduced in every session of Congress since 1923, finally got out of committee and onto the floor. The time seemed right for an amendment guaranteeing equality of rights under the law without regard to sex. The House passed the ERA in 1971 by a huge margin, and in 1972 the Senate followed suit. Congress then sent the ERA to the states for approval, with the usual seven-year deadline for getting the necessary three-fourths majority—38 states.

Ratification seemed a foregone conclusion. Within three months, 20 states rushed to pass the ERA. Within a year, 30 states were in the fold. The bandwagon was rolling, with six years left to get only 8 more states' approval.

By 1973, though, major opposition had surfaced. Conservatives saw the ERA as a threat to family life and the traditional division of tasks between the sexes. They feared that current marriage, divorce, and child-custody laws would be thrown out under ERA provisions. They felt that

existing laws already protected women's interests that needed protecting—hiring, promotions, and pay—so a "Stop ERA" campaign was organized.

In 1974 three states ratified the ERA, but in 1975 only one did. There were no ratifications in 1976; in 1977 one final state ratified the ERA. Thus, in 1979, the ERA became the first constitutional amendment ever to end its seven-year limit unratified. Backers were shocked.

Then, in a move without precedent, Congress extended the time for ratification by three years. The extra time did not help, though. In fact, five states tried to rescind—cancel—their ratifications, though Congress did not permit them to do so. Also, the election of Ronald Reagan as president in 1980 confirmed a shift to conservative thinking in the nation.

Not one state passed the ERA during the extra three years, and in 1982 the second deadline expired. The issue died for good on November 12, 1983, when the U.S. House fell six votes short on a revival bill that would have created an ERA II.

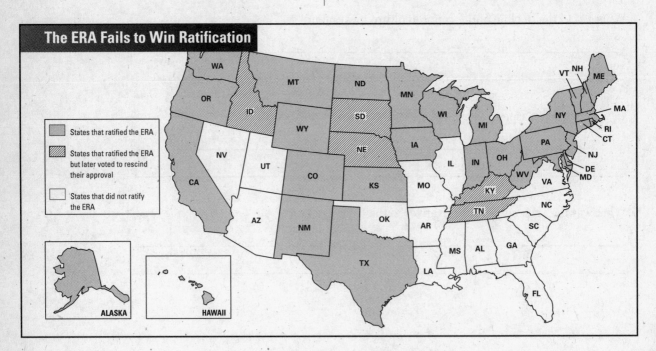

The ERA Fails to Win Ratification

States that ratified the ERA

States that ratified the ERA but later voted to rescind their approval

States that did not ratify the ERA

Interpreting Text and Visuals

1. State in your own words the goal of the attempt to add an Equal Rights
   Amendment to the Constitution. _____

   _____

   _____

2. How many states voted to ratify the ERA? _____

3. Why did ratification of the ERA seem a sure thing in 1974? _____

   _____

   _____

   _____

4. Which states tried to rescind their ERA ratifications? _____

   Which states, if any, had their attempts to withdraw ratification upheld? _____

   _____

5. Which region of the United States was solidly against the ERA? _____

   What two other regions seem to have shown some resistance to the ERA? _____

   _____

6. What two unprecedented events occurred in connection with the ERA voting?

   _____

   _____

   _____

   _____

7. How would the ERA have fared if ratifying an amendment had required only a
   three-fifths majority of states? _____

   a two-thirds majority of states? _____

CHAPTER
23
SECTION 1

PRIMARY SOURCE *The Farm Worker Movement*

César Chávez, himself a former migrant worker, and Dolores Huerta established the National Farm Workers Association (NFWA) in 1962 to bargain for higher wages and other benefits. This is Chavez's account of the NFWA's first strike.

We had our first strike in the spring of 1965. While we didn't win, it gave us a good indication of what to expect in other strikes, how labor contractors and police would be used against us.

Epifanio Camacho, a farm worker from McFarland, just south of Delano, came and told us of all the abuses in the rose industry there. We worked with those workers for more than a month until we had them tightly organized.

Grafting roses is highly skilled work. Grafters crawl on their knees for miles slitting mature rose bushes and inserting buds at top speed. The slightest miscalculation means the bud will not take and the bush will be useless.

Although they were promised $9 a thousand plants, injertadors—grafters of roses—were actually getting between $6.50 and $7 a thousand.

After a series of meetings to prepare the strike, we chose the biggest company, Mount Arbor, which employed about eighty-five workers, not counting the irrigators and supervisors. We voted not to have a picket line, because everyone pledged not to break the strike.

We had a pledge ceremony on Sunday, the day before the strike started. Dolores held the crucifix, and the guys put their hands on it, pledging not to break the strike.

Early Monday morning we sent out ten cars to check the people's homes. We found lights in five or six places and knocked on the doors. The men were getting up.

"Where are you going?" we asked them.

Most of them were embarrassed. "Oh, I was just getting up, you know."

"You're not going to work are you?"

"Of course not!"

The company foreman was very angry when none of the grafters showed up for work. He refused to talk to us. Thinking that maybe a woman would have a better chance, we had Dolores knock on the office door about 10:30.

"Get out, you Communist! Get out," the manager shouted.

I guess they were expecting us, because as Dolores was arguing with him, the cops came and told her to leave.

A day or so later, we had a hunch two or three workers living in one house were going to break the strike. So Dolores drove up to their driveway in a green truck, killed the motor, put it in gear, set the brake, locked the windows and doors, took the keys, and hid them so they couldn't drive out. Even though she was alone, she refused to move.

Then a group of Mexican workers from Tangansiguiero helped break the strike. Everybody was angry, and we sent a letter to the mayor of Tangansiguiero denouncing them. In those little Mexican towns, they have an old building where people go to read the news. On one side they list things like stray animals, and on the other they have a list of criminals.

The mayor was so upset, he put our letter on the side with the criminals, in effect classifying them as such. We got immediate reactions from the workers. People came and said, "Don't be like that. You're giving me a bad name in my community when I go back."

And I said, "Look, you broke the strike. You deserve that and more."

from Jacques E. Levy, *César Chávez: Autobiography of La Causa* (New York: Norton, 1975), 179–180.

Discussion Questions

1. Why did the NFWA decide to organize a strike against Mount Arbor?
2. How did Chávez and Huerta try to keep the strike from being broken?
3. Do you think that strikes and boycotts effectively promoted *La Causa*? Why or why not? Cite evidence from your textbook to support your opinion.

Name _____ Date _____

PRIMARY SOURCE *United Farm Workers Poster*

This poster advertises a 1968 benefit performance for the United Farm Workers Union. Examine the poster and then answer the questions below.

Museum of American Political Life, University of Hartford, West Hartford, CT.
Photo by Sally Andersen-Bruce.

Discussion Questions

1. Where was the benefit performance to be held?
2. Who were some of the celebrities who were scheduled to perform?

3. What message do you think this poster was meant to convey? Think about the purpose of the benefit performance as well as what's on the poster.

PRIMARY SOURCE *from The Feminine Mystique*

As you read this excerpt from Betty Friedan's landmark book, think about her definition of the "feminine mystique" and its impact on the lives of American women.

The feminine mystique says that the highest value and the only commitment for women is the fulfillment of their own femininity. It says that the great mistake of Western culture, through most of its history, has been the undervaluation of this femininity. It says this femininity is so mysterious and intuitive and close to the creation and origin of life that man-made science may never be able to understand it. But however special and different, it is in no way inferior to the nature of man; it may even in certain respects be superior. The mistake, says the mystique, the root of women's troubles in the past is that women envied men, women tried to be like men, instead of accepting their own nature, which can find fulfillment only in sexual passivity, male domination, and nurturing maternal love.

But the new image this mystique gives to American women is the old image: "Occupation: housewife." The new mystique makes the housewife-mothers, who never had a chance to be anything else, the model for all women; it presupposes that history has reached a final and glorious end in the here and now, as far as women are concerned. Beneath the sophisticated trappings, it simply makes certain concrete, finite, domestic aspects of feminine existence—as it was lived by women whose lives were confined, by necessity, to cooking, cleaning, washing, bearing children—into a religion, a pattern by which all women must now live or deny their femininity.

Fulfillment as a woman had only one definition for American women after 1949—the housewife-mother. As swiftly as in a dream, the image of the American woman as a changing, growing individual in a changing world was shattered. Her solo flight to find her own identity was forgotten in the rush for the security of togetherness. Her limitless world shrunk to the cozy walls of home. . . .

The material details of life, the daily burden of cooking and cleaning, or taking care of the physical needs of husband and children—these did indeed define a woman's world a century ago when Americans were pioneers, and the American frontier lay in conquering the land. But the women who went west with the wagon trains also shared the pioneering purpose. Now the American frontiers are of the mind, and of the spirit. Love and children and home are good, but they are not the whole world. . . . Why should women accept this picture of a half-life, instead of a share in the whole of human destiny? Why should women try to make housework "something more," instead of moving on the frontiers of their own time, as American women moved beside their husbands on the old frontiers?

A baked potato is not as big as the world, and vacuuming the living room floor—with or without makeup—is not work that takes enough thought or energy to challenge any woman's full capacity. Women are human beings, not stuffed dolls, not animals. . . .

It is more than a strange paradox that as all professions are finally open to women in America, "career woman" has become a dirty word; that as higher education becomes available to any woman with the capacity for it, education for women has become so suspect that more and more drop out of high school and college to marry and have babies; that as so many roles in modern society become theirs for the taking, women so insistently confine themselves to one role. Why, with the removal of all the legal, political, economic, and educational barriers that once kept woman from being man's equal, a person in her own right, an individual free to develop her own potential, should she accept this new image which insists she is not a person but a "woman," by definition barred from the freedom of human existence and a voice in human destiny?

from Betty Friedan, *The Feminine Mystique* (New York: Norton, 1963), 43–44, 66–68.

Research Option

Work with a small group of classmates to find statistics related to the marital status, education, employment, income, and so forth of American women today. Then draw conclusions about how women today compare with those described in this excerpt.

CHAPTER

23

Section 3

PRIMARY SOURCE *Popular Song*

"Woodstock" was written by the singer and songwriter Joni Mitchell. In the 1970s the version recorded by Crosby, Stills, Nash and Young climbed to number 11 on the pop charts. This song not only captures the spirit of the Woodstock music festival but also the search for deeper meaning that marked much of the 1960s.

Woodstock

I came upon a child of God; he was walking along the road
And I asked him, "Where are you going?"
This he told me: "I'm going on down to Yasgur's Farm,
Gonna join in a rock and roll band.
I'm gonna camp out on the land and try 'n' get my soul free."
    We are stardust, we are golden
    And we got to get ourselves back to the garden.
"Then can I walk beside you? I have come here to lose the smog
And I feel to be a cog in something turning.
Maybe it is just the time of year, or maybe it's the time of man.
I don't know who I am, but life is for learning."
    We are stardust, we are golden
    And we got to get ourselves back to the garden.
By the time we got to Woodstock we were half a million strong
And ev'rywhere was song and celebration.
And I dreamed I saw the bombers riding shotgun in the sky,
Turning into butterflies above our nation.
    We are stardust, billion year old carbon,
    Caught in the devil's bargain
    And we got to get ourselves back to the garden.

from Joni Mitchell, "Woodstock." Copyright © 1969, 1974 by Siquomb Publishing Corp.

Activity Options

1. Listen to a recording of "Woodstock." Then share your impressions with your classmates. What mood does the song reflect? What do you think the lyrics mean? How do the lyrics and music capture the spirit of the 1960s in general and Woodstock in particular?

2. Design a cover for a single CD recording of "Woodstock." Then share your design with the class.

3. Play another recording for the class that evokes the counterculture movement, including other music associated with the festival at Woodstock.

CHAPTER 23

Section 1

LITERATURE SELECTION *from Los Vendidos*
by Luis Valdez

El Teatro Campesino (The Fieldworkers' Theater), founded by Luis Valdez to support a farm workers' strike against grape growers, first performed Los Vendidos *in 1967 in an East Los Angeles park. This one-act play, or* acto, *satirizes Latino stereotypes in order to inspire audiences to social action. What stereotypes does Valdez portray in this excerpt?*

Scene: Honest Sancho's *Used Mexican Lot and Mexican Curio Shop. Three models are on display in* Honest Sancho's *shop. To the right, there is a* Revolucionario, *complete with sombrero, carrilleras, and carabina 30–30. At center, on the floor, there is the* Farmworker, *under a broad straw sombrero. At stage left is the* Pachuco, *filero in hand.* Honest Sancho *is moving among his models, dusting them off and preparing for another day of business.*

SANCHO: Bueno, bueno, mis monos, vamos a ver a quién vendemos ahora, ¿no? *(To audience.)* ¡Quihubo! I'm Honest Sancho and this is my shop. Antes fui contratista, pero ahora logré tener mi negocito. All I need now is a customer. *(A bell rings offstage.)* Ay, a customer!

SECRETARY: *(Entering.)* Good morning, I'm Miss Jimenez from . . .

SANCHO: Ah, una chicana! Welcome, welcome, Señorita Jimenez.

SECRETARY: *(Anglo pronunciation.)* JIM-enez.

SANCHO: ¿Qué?

SECRETARY: My name is Miss JIM-enez. Don't you speak English? What's wrong with you?

SANCHO: Oh, nothing. Señorita JIM-enez. I'm here to help you.

SECRETARY: That's better. As I was starting to say, I'm a secretary from Governor Reagan's office, and we're looking for a Mexican type for the administration.

SANCHO: Well, you come to the right place, lady. This is Honest Sancho's Used Mexican Lot, and we got all types here. Any particular type you want?

SECRETARY: Yes, we were looking for somebody suave . . .

SANCHO: Suave.

SECRETARY: Debonaire.

SANCHO: De buen aire.

SECRETARY: Dark.

SANCHO: Prieto.

SECRETARY: But of course, not too dark.

SANCHO: No muy prieto.

SECRETARY: Perhaps, beige.

SANCHO: Beige, just the tone. Asi como cafecito con leche, ¿no?

SECRETARY: One more thing. He must be hard-working.

SANCHO: That could only be one model. Step right over here to the center of the shop, lady. *(They cross to the* Farmworker.*)* This is our standard farmworker model. As you can see, in the words of our beloved Senator George Murphy, he is "built close to the ground." Also, take special notice of his 4-ply Goodyear huaraches, made from the rain tire. This wide-brimmed sombrero is an extra added feature; keeps off the sun, rain and dust.

SECRETARY: Yes, it does look durable.

SANCHO: And our farmworker model is friendly. Muy amable. Watch. *(Snaps his fingers.)*

FARMWORKER: *(Lifts up head.)* Buenos días, señorita. *(His head drops.)*

SECRETARY: My, he is friendly.

SANCHO: Didn't I tell you? Loves his patrones! But his most attractive feature is that he's hard-working. Let me show you. *(Snaps fingers.* Farmworker *stands.)*

FARMWORKER: ¡El jale! *(He begins to work.)*

SANCHO: As you can see he is cutting grapes.

SECRETARY: Oh, I wouldn't know.

SANCHO: He also picks cotton. *(Snaps.* Farmworker *begins to pick cotton.)*

SECRETARY: Versatile, isn't he?

SANCHO: He also picks melons. *(Snaps.* Farmworker *picks melons.)* That's his slow speed for late in the season. Here's his fast speed. *(Snap.* Farmworker *picks faster.)*

SECRETARY: Chihuahua . . . I mean, goodness, he sure is a hardworker. . . . But is he economical?

SANCHO: Economical? Señorita, you are looking at the Volkswagen of Mexicans. Pennies a day is all it takes. One plate of beans and tortillas will keep him going all day. That, and chile. Plenty of chile jalapeños, chile verde, chile colorado . . .

SECRETARY: What about storage?

SANCHO: No problem. You know these new farm labor camps our Honorable Governor Reagan has built out by Parlier or Raisin City? They were designed with our model in mind. Five, six, seven, even ten in one of those shacks will give you no trouble at all. You can also put him in old barns, old cars, riverbanks. You can even leave him out in the field over night with no worry!

SECRETARY: Remarkable.

SANCHO: And here's an added feature: every year at the end of the season, this model goes back to Mexico and doesn't return, automatically, until next spring.

SECRETARY: How about that. But tell me, does he speak English?

SANCHO: Another outstanding feature is that last year this model was programmed to go out on STRIKE! *(Snap.)*

FARMWORKER: ¡Huelga! ¡Huelga! Hermanos, sálganse de esos files. *(Snap. He stops.)*

SECRETARY: No! Oh no, we can't strike in the State Capitol.

SANCHO: Well, he also scabs. *(Snap.)*

FARMWORKER: Me vendo barato, ¿y qué? *(Snap.)*

SECRETARY: That's much better, but you didn't answer my question. Does he speak English?

SANCHO: Bueno . . . no, pero he has other . . .

SECRETARY: No.

SANCHO: Other features.

SECRETARY: No! He just won't do!

SANCHO: Okay, okay, pues. We have other models.

SECRETARY: I hope so. What we need is something a little more sophisticated. . . .

[He shows her the Pachuco and Revolucionario models, both of which she rejects.]

SECRETARY: You still don't understand what we need. It's true we need Mexican models, such as these, but it's more important that he be American.

SANCHO: American?

SECRETARY: That's right, and judging from what you've shown me, I don't think you have what we want. Well, my lunch hour's almost over, I better . . .

SANCHO: Wait a minute! Mexican but American?

SECRETARY: That's correct.

SANCHO: Mexican but . . . *(A sudden flash.)* American! Yeah, I think we've got exactly what you want. He just came in today! Give me a minute. *(He exits. Talks from backstage.)* Here he is in the shop. Let me just get some papers off. There. Introducing our new 1970 Mexican-American! Ta-ra-ra-raaaa! *(Sancho brings out the Mexican-American model, a clean-shaven middle class type in a business suit, with glasses.)*

SECRETARY: *(Impressed.)* Where have you been hiding this one?

SANCHO: He just came in this morning. Ain't he a beauty? Feast your eyes on him! Sturdy U.S. Steel Frame, streamlined, modern. As a matter of fact, he is built exactly like our Anglo models, except that he comes in a variety of darker shades: naugahide, leather or leatherette.

SECRETARY: Naugahide.

SANCHO: Well, we'll just write that down. Yes, señorita, this model represents the apex of American engineering! He is bilingual, college educated, ambitious! He is intelligent, well-mannered, clean. . . . *(Snap. Mexican-American turns toward Sancho.)* Eric? *(To Secretary.)* We call him Eric García. *(To Eric.)* I want you to meet Miss JIM-enez, Eric.

MEXICAN-AMERICAN: Miss JIM-enez, I am delighted to make your acquaintance. *(He kisses her hand.)*

SECRETARY: Oh, my, how charming!

SANCHO: Did you feel the suction? He has seven especially engineered suction cups right behind his lips. He's a charmer all right!

SECRETARY: How about boards, does he function on boards?

SANCHO: You name them, he is on them. Parole boards, draft boards, school boards, taco quality control boards, surf boards, two by fours.

SECRETARY: Does he function in politics?

SANCHO: Señorita, you are looking at a political machine. Have you ever heard of the OEO, EOC, COD, WAR ON POVERTY? That's our model! Not only that, he makes political speeches!

SECRETARY: May I hear one?

SANCHO: With pleasure. *(Snap.)* Eric, give us a speech.

MEXICAN-AMERICAN: Mr. Congressman, Mr. Chairman, members of the board, honored guests, ladies and gentlemen. *(Sancho and Secretary applaud.)* Please, please. I come before you as a Mexican-American to tell you about the problems of the Mexican. The problems of the Mexican stem from one thing and one thing only: he's stupid. He's uneducated. He needs to stay in school. He needs to be ambitious, forward-looking, harder-working. He needs to think American, American, American, American, American! God bless America! God bless America! God bless America! (*He goes out of control.* Sancho *snaps frantically and the Mexican-American finally slumps forward, bending at the waist.*)

SECRETARY: Oh my, he's patriotic too!

SANCHO: Sí, señorita, he loves his country. Let me just make a little adjustment here. (*Stands Mexican-American up.*)

SECRETARY: What about upkeep? Is he economical?

SANCHO: Well, no, I won't lie to you. The Mexican-American costs a little bit more, but you get what you pay for. He's worth every extra cent. You can keep him running on dry Martinis, Langendorf bread . . .

SECRETARY: Apple pie?

SANCHO: Only Mom's. Of course, he's also programmed to eat Mexican food at ceremonial functions, but I must warn you, an overdose of beans will plug up his exhaust.

SECRETARY: Fine! There's just one more question. How much do you want for him?

SANCHO: Well, I tell you what I'm gonna do. Today and today only, because you've been so sweet, I'm gonna let you steal this model from me! I'm gonna let you drive him off the lot for the simple price of, let's see, taxes and license included, $15,000.

SECRETARY: Fifteen thousand dollars? For a Mexican!!!!

SANCHO: Mexican? What are you talking about? This is a Mexican-American! We had to melt down two pachucos, a farmworker and three gabachos to make this model! You want quality, but you gotta pay for it! This is no cheap runabout. He's got class!

SECRETARY: Okay, I'll take him.

SANCHO: You will?

SECRETARY: Here's your money.

SANCHO: You mind if I count it?

SECRETARY: Go right ahead.

SANCHO: Well, you'll get your pink slip in the mail. Oh, do you want me to wrap him up for you? We have a box in the back.

SECRETARY: No, thank you. The Governor is having a luncheon this afternoon, and we need a brown face in the crowd. How do I drive him?

SANCHO: Just snap your fingers. He'll do anything you want. (Secretary *snaps.* Mexican-American *steps forward.*)

MEXICAN-AMERICAN: ¡Raza querida, vamos levantando armas para liberarnos de estos desgraciados gabachos que nos explotan! Vamos . . .

SECRETARY: What did he say?

SANCHO: Something about taking up arms . . . [against] white people, etc.

SECRETARY: But he's not supposed to say that!

SANCHO: Look, lady, don't blame me for bugs from the factory. He's your Mexican-American, you bought him, now drive him off the lot!

Activity Options

1. With your classmates, discuss what stereotypes Valdez satirizes in this excerpt and why it is important to recognize—and reject—such stereotypes.

2. This *acto* reflects political and social issues that concerned Latinos in the 1960s. Write a satirical sketch in the style of *Los Vendidos* about an aspect of today's society that you would like to change.

3. The first *actos* were often improvised by striking farm workers and performed with a few simple props in parks and meeting halls. Create a playbill—a poster that announces a theatrical production—for a performance of *Los Vendidos* in keeping with the social purpose and spirit of *actos.*

CHAPTER 23

Section 1

AMERICAN LIVES César Chávez
Organizing for Action

"I am convinced that the truest act of courage, the strongest act of manliness, is to sacrifice ourselves for others in a totally nonviolent struggle for justice."
—César Chávez, on ending a hunger strike, 1968

César Chávez (1927–1993) grew up seeing migrant farm workers suffer from low pay and poor conditions. Consequently he dedicated his adult life to improving the lives of oppressed farm workers. By working tirelessly and using nonviolence, he built the first successful union of farm workers. In his obituary in the New York Times, Chávez was depicted as humble, with an air that was "almost religious"; his $5 weekly salary was described as "a virtual vow of poverty."

In the 1920s Chávez's parents toiled on their small farm near Yuma, Arizona. (His grandparents had migrated from Mexico in 1880.) Then Chavez's father lost the farm in the Depression, and the family moved to California to pick crops. There young Chávez watched his father join every agricultural union that came along, though none survived long. Through him, Chávez came to understand what was required to organize farm workers successfully: a long-term effort and close personal contact.

In the 1950s, Chávez met two people who changed his life. One was a Catholic priest who increased his knowledge of labor history and his devotion to the principles of nonviolence. The other was a social activist from a group called the Community Service Organization (CSO). Chávez learned from him how to organize.

Although very shy, Chávez became an excellent CSO recruiter. He started twenty-two chapters in California and became the CSO's general director. However, he felt that the CSO was not committed enough to the farm workers. He left the CSO in 1962 and used his small savings to launch a new union of farm workers.

Each night after a long day's work in the fields, Chávez met with farm workers in their homes. He was so poor that he often had to beg for food for his family from the workers he tried to recruit. After two years, he had about a thousand members in his National Farm Workers Association (NFWA). In 1965, the union won wage increases from two small growers. That year, the Department of Labor ordered that growers had to pay $1.40 an hour to workers brought in from Mexico. This was more than American farm workers—whether Filipino, Mexican, or white—earned. A group of Filipino workers led by Larry Itliong struck to demand an equal wage. Chávez did not want to break the strike, but he did not believe that his union was strong enough to strike yet. Still, he put the issue to a vote. NFWA members chose to join the strike.

Soon Chávez and Itliong agreed to merge their organizations to have a stronger force. Finally, the union won contracts with the companies that grew grapes for wine. It was a remarkable success—but only a partial one. Table grape growers still refused to recognize the union.

Chávez staged a national grape boycott. The strike dragged on for many months. Over that time, Chávez tried to ensure that his workers upheld the principles of nonviolent protest that he valued. When he felt that union members were becoming too angry, he staged a hunger strike. For 25 days he refused to eat as he rededicated himself—and the union—to nonviolence. As the strike continued, support for the boycott grew. Finally, the growers agreed to recognize the union. It took almost five years, but NFWA won better wages and working conditions for its members.

Chávez's work was not completed, however. In later years, he fought growers' efforts to install a rival union that would accept less expensive contracts. He also tried to organize lettuce pickers. When he died in 1993, he was on the road in Arizona supporting another union effort.

Questions

1. Why did Chávez once say that acting in a nonviolent way is the "truest act of courage"?
2. What obstacles blocked migrant workers' efforts to organize?
3. What sacrifices did Chávez make for the union cause?

AMERICAN LIVES Betty Friedan
Launching a Movement

Section 2   *"[We will act] to bring women into full participation in American society now, exercising all the privileges and responsibilities thereof in truly equal partnership with men."—National Organization for Women, Statement of Purpose, 1966*

The 1963 book *The Feminine Mystique* helped launch the modern feminist movement. By describing the frustration many women felt at being confined to the role of wife and mother, the author, Betty Friedan (b. 1921), helped women see that they were not alone.

Betty Goldstein studied psychology in college and graduated with highest honors. Over the next few years, she did some graduate study, worked in journalism, and married Carl Friedan. When she was pregnant in 1954 with her second child, she asked for maternity leave. She was fired instead.

Over the next decade, Friedan mixed raising her children with occasional writing of magazine articles. She became frustrated because editors did not want articles about women with careers. They would print only stories about women's home lives. In 1957, Friedan began to survey her college classmates. She wondered, fifteen years after graduation, how they felt about their lives. The results of her study launched a movement.

Friedan found that many women in her study were frustrated by the barriers that society placed in their paths. The "feminine mystique" forced women to focus on family alone, not on careers. She published her findings in *The Feminine Mystique*. At first, the publisher printed only 2,000 copies. In ten years, the book sold in the millions.

The book came at a time when unfairness against women was coming to light. That same year, a government commission report criticized society's treatment of women. In response, Congress passed a law requiring that women receive equal pay for equal work. Friedan's book helped spur women to take action.

In 1964 Congress was debating the Civil Rights Act. One member added an amendment that would ban job discrimination against women. He did it to try to defeat the act. However, the act—and the ban—passed. A new government agency was set up to enforce the law, but it refused to act on cases of discrimination against women. In 1966, Friedan and others took action of their own. They formed the National Organization for Women (NOW). The group vowed to push the government to enforce the law.

NOW chose Friedan as president, and she gave the group a solid start. Within five years, NOW grew to more than 15,000 members. Over time, though, some members urged a more radical program than Friedan supported. By 1970, she felt that these members had gained control of the group, and she left the presidency. She did not leave the fight for women's rights, though. Later in 1970 she organized a nationwide strike for equality. She campaigned for the Equal Rights Amendment (ERA). Many feminists wanted this amendment to the Constitution to guarantee equal rights for women. The ERA was never ratified, however. Friedan blamed, in part, the radicals of NOW for its defeat. She said that their ideas—outside the mainstream of American thought—cost the ERA badly needed support.

Since then Friedan has continued to travel, lecture, and write. She created a storm of protest in 1981 with her book *The Second Stage*. In it she tried to move feminism back into the American mainstream. Women had lost something from the feminist emphasis on careers, she said. What was needed was a way of balancing career and family, not the emphasis of either over the other. Some feminists said she had abandoned the cause. Others defended her for recognizing that life includes work and family. In 1993 she published *The Fountain of Age*. The book examined human vitality after age 60 and criticized nursing-home operators.

Questions

1. How did magazines help spread the "feminine mystique"?
2. One feminist said that Friedan had the same impact on women that Martin Luther King, Jr., had on African Americans. How were the effects of their lives similar?
3. Why did some feminists criticize Friedan for the ideas in *The Second Stage?*

Answer Key

Chapter 20, Section 1
GUIDED READING

A. Possible answers:

1. Voter restlessness; an economic recession; Kennedy's poise during the TV debate; Kennedy's frankness about the religious issue; coming to the aid of Martin Luther King, Jr.; his good looks and charisma; his well-organized campaign; the Kennedy family's wealth

2. Invaders killed or jailed; Kennedy embarrassed; a public relations triumph for Castro; ransom paid for release of invaders

3. The Berlin Wall built; the flow of refugees reduced

4. Khrushchev's prestige damaged; Kennedy criticized; Cuban exiles switched allegiance from the Democratic party to the G.O.P.; Castro banned flights between Cuba and Miami

5. To enable U.S. and Soviet leaders to communicate at once should another crisis arise

6. Ban the explosion of nuclear devices in the atmosphere

B. Answers will vary widely depending upon the specifics noted.

Chapter 20, Section 2
GUIDED READING

A. Possible answers:

1. Beliefs: Increased spending; engaged in deficit spending; lower taxes

   Results: Congress increased defense spending, increased the minimum wage, extended unemployment insurance, and provided assistance to cities with high unemployment.

2. Beliefs: Offered volunteer, economic, and technical assistance to developing nations

   Results: the Peace Corps; the Alliance for Progress; some economic progress in developing nations

3. Beliefs: Set the goal of landing on the moon before the end of 1960s; increased spending on the space program

   Results: U.S. astronauts orbited the Earth and finally landed on the moon; science programs expanded;

new industries; new technological developments; the rapid growth of Southern and Western states

4. Medical care for the aged; rebuilding of blighted urban areas; federal aid for education

5. A "national assault on poverty"; an investigation of racial injustice in the South; a national civil rights bill; a tax cut

B. Answers will vary widely depending upon the specifics noted.

Chapter 20, Section 3
GUIDED READING

A. Possible answers:

1. Tax-cut: Economic growth; an increase in consumer spending, business investment, and tax revenues; a reduction in federal budget deficit

2. Civil Rights: Prohibited discrimination based on race, religion, national origin, and gender; granted the federal government new powers of enforcement

3. Economic: Funded youth programs, antipoverty measures, small business loans, and job training; created the Job Corps, the VISTA volunteer program, Project Head Start, and the Community Action Program

4. Education: Provided federal aid to help public and parochial schools to purchase textbooks and new library materials and to offer special education classes

5. Medicare: Provided hospital and low-cost medical insurance to most Americans age 65 or older

6. Medicaid: Extended health insurance to welfare recipients

7. Immigration: Replaced the national origins system with a new immigration quota system that allowed more non-European immigrants to settle in the U.S.

B. Possible answers:

1. Brown: Ruled that school segregation is unconstitutional

2. Baker: Established the principle of "one person, one vote"; asserted that federal courts had the right to tell states to reapportion districts for more equal representation

3. Mapp: Ruled that evidence seized

illegally could not be used in state courts—the "exclusionary rule"

4. Gideon: Required criminal courts to provide legal counsel to those who could not afford it

5. Escobedo: Ruled that an accused person has the right to have a lawyer present during questioning

6. Miranda: Ruled that all suspects must be "read their rights" before questioning; established the Miranda rights

Chapter 20
BUILDING VOCABULARY

A.

1. c	2. d
3. a	4. e
5. f	6. b

B.

1. b	2. b	3. a
4. c	5. a	

C. Answers will vary depending on the specifics noted.

Chapter 20, Section 1
SKILLBUILDER PRACTICE

Possible responses:

1. generally went up throughout the period shown

2. that viewing time would continue to rise (Note: You might challenge students to check their predictions by looking up figures for the late 1990s in the most recent edition of the *Information Please Almanac*.)

3. Answers will vary, but most students will probably correlate increased television viewing time with increased spending on television advertisement.

Chapter 20, Section 1
RETEACHING ACTIVITY

A. April 1861—Bay of Pigs invasion / U.S. fails to overthrow Castro and young Kennedy administration appears inept; August 1961—Berlin Wall Crisis; aggravates Cold War tensions and becomes prominent symbol of Communist oppression;

October 1962—Cuban Missile Crisis; U.S. and Soviets move to the brink of war before pulling back; U.S. and Soviets try to ease Cold War tensions with hot line and Limited Test Ban Treaty

B.

1. Richard Nixon
2. Robert Kennedy
3. defense spending
4. Green Berets

Chapter 20, Section 2
RETEACHING ACTIVITY

1. deficit spending; the administration increased the budget for the Department of the Defense by 20 percent and increased spending on various social programs

2. The Peace Corps provided assistance to developing nations around the world, while the Alliance for Progress focused mainly on Latin America.

3. It prompted many universities to expand their science programs; it gave rise to new industries and developments, and led to the growth of many Southern and Western states—where many defense-related industries were located.

4. A conservative coalition of Republicans and Southern Democrats blocked many of Kennedy's measures; Kennedy felt he did not have a mandate to push through his programs

5. to improve relations with the conservative state's Democratic Party

6. The assassin, Lee Harvey Oswald, had acted on his own.

Chapter 20, Section 3
RETEACHING ACTIVITY

1. d	2. a
3. b	4. b
5. c	6. a

Chapter 20, Section 1
GEOGRAPHY APPLICATION

Responses may vary on the inferential questions. Sample responses are given for those.

1. West Germany
2. the Western powers
3. East Germany
4. about 80 miles; though a part of West Germany, West Berlin was completely surrounded by hostile territory, and protecting its citizens' freedom must have been difficult.
5. East Germany; to prevent people from escaping from East Germany by way of West Berlin
6. A resident of Leipzig might have found it easier to get into West Berlin and fly from there to Munich than to attempt an overland crossing of the border between East Germany and West Germany.
7. Cages are meant to prevent the escape of the animals or people inside, but the "cage" around West Berlin was meant to prevent the escape of the people outside. It was the people inside who were free.

Chapter 20, Section 1
PRIMARY SOURCE

John F. Kennedy's Inaugural Address

1. Informally assess students' choice and reading of passages.
2. Informally assess students' ideas and action plans. You may want them to carry out a project that benefits the school or their community.

Chapter 20, Section 1
PRIMARY SOURCE

Political Cartoon

Possible responses:

1. They must work together to ensure that nuclear war does not happen. The cartoon also implies that no one people—neither Americans nor Soviets—is immune from the dangers of nuclear war.

2. Some students may feel that the cartoon's spirit is overly optimistic because years of Cold War tensions between the Soviet Union and the United States could not be so easily erased. On the other hand, students may point out that Kennedy and

Krushchev had already gone to the brink of nuclear war during the Cuban missile crisis but stopped in time and then demonstrated in 1963 that they were willing to work together to ease tensions by establishing a hot line and by agreeing to a Limited Test Ban Treaty.

Chapter 20, Section 3
PRIMARY SOURCE

Unsafe at Any Speed

1. Through their research, students may find that according to the National Safety Council there were 42,700 highway fatalities in 1994 and 43,900 in 1995. They may conclude that in 30 years the situation described by Nader has somewhat improved in terms of total number of deaths annually attributed to motor vehicles.

2. Through research, students will find that Nader's testimony before Congress in 1966 persuaded lawmakers to pass the National Traffic and Motor Vehicle Safety Act. They may infer that Nader's insistence on establishing automobile safety standards in the 1960s is indirectly responsible for safety features in cars today such as airbags, running lights, and antilock brakes.

Chapter 20, Section 2
LITERATURE SELECTION

Paper Wings

1. Encourage groups to record their interviews. Have students turn in taped or transcribed interviews. Then informally assess their work.

2. Before students begin, you may want to brainstorm recent events of local, national, or international importance. Then informally assess students' personal narratives.

3. Informally assess students' participation in the class discussion.

Chapter 20, Section 2
AMERICAN LIVES

Alan Shepard

Possible responses:

1. In the climate of the Cold War, these first U.S. astronauts were seen

as heroes who would meet the challenge of Soviet space advances.

2. The government allowed the live broadcast of Shepard's flight to help generate enthusiasm for the space program.

3. In favor: Sending a person to land on the moon was worthwhile because it established a goal that people could unite behind. Opposed: The money could have been better spent trying to solve problems in society.

Chapter 20, Section 3
AMERICAN LIVES

Rachel Carson

Possible responses:

1. People thought that DDT was highly beneficial because it destroyed disease-carrying insects. They didn't know about its dangers.

2. She could have been referring to the quiet that would result from birds dying due to contamination.

3. Chemical companies made money by selling DDT, so Carson's book was a threat to them.

Chapter 21, Section 1
GUIDED READING

Possible answers:

1. Outlawed segregation in public facilities

2. Upheld Louisiana's "separate but equal" law as constitutional

3. a. the war opened up job opportunities for African Americans

   b. African-American soldiers returned home determined to fight for their own freedom

   c. during the war, organizations had campaigned for civil rights.

4. Thurgood Marshall; NAACP

5. That segregation is unconstitutional

6. The Montgomery Improvement Association

7. Organized a boycott of Montgomery buses

8. Placed the Arkansas National Guard under federal control; ordered in paratroopers

9. Martin Luther King, Jr.

10. To "carry on nonviolent crusades" against racism

11. Desegregated lunch counters; sit-ins

Chapter 21, Section 2
GUIDED READING

A. Possible answers:

1. To test Supreme Court decisions banning segregation on interstate bus routes and facilities in bus terminals

2. Sent U.S. marshals to protect them; issued an order banning segregation in all interstate travel facilities

3. To persuade Congress to pass Kennedy's civil rights bill

4. 250,000 civil rights supporters, including 75,000 whites

5. To register African-American voters who could elect pro-civil rights legislators

6. 1,000 college students; SNCC staff members

7. Convinced people from across the nation to join the marchers

8. To ask Congress for the swift passage of a voting rights bill

9. Eliminated the illiteracy test; stated that federal examiners could enroll voters denied suffrage by local officials

10. Tripled the number of registered African-American voters in the South; raised the registration of eligible African-American voters in the U.S. from 10% in 1964 to 60% in 1968

B. Answers will vary widely depending upon the specifics noted.

Chapter 21, Section 3
GUIDED READING

A. Possible answers:

1. De facto segregation exists by practice and custom; de jure segregation exists by law.

2. SNCC believed in nonviolent civil disobedience and racial harmony. The Nation of Islam believed that whites were evil and that blacks should separate from white society;

it advocated the use of armed self-defense.

3. Early on, Malcolm X believed in the teachings of the Nation of Islam; later, his attitude toward whites softened, and he advocated the use of ballots over bullets.

4. Carmichael was an organizer for SNCC and later became a Black Panther.

5. SNCC believed in nonviolent civil disobedience and racial harmony; the Black Panthers advocated black nationalism, black power, and armed revolt.

6. Any four of the following: increased pride and awareness of racial identity among many African Americans; new college programs in African-American history and literature; greater visibility of African Americans in movies and on TV; ended de jure segregation; the passage of civil rights laws; an increased awareness of de facto segregation; the integration of educational facilities; significant increases in the number of African Americans who finished high school and went to college; a significant increase in the number of African-American voters; a significant increase in the number of elected African-American officials; the growth of affirmative action programs

B. Answers will vary widely depending upon the specifics noted.

Chapter 21
BUILDING VOCABULARY

A.

1. d	2. h	3. g
4. f	5. a	6. c
7. e	8. b	

B.

1. freedom summer
2. literacy tests
3. Stokely Carmichael
4. Kerner Commission
5. schools

C. Answers will vary depending on the specifics noted.

Chapter 21, Section 1
SKILLBUILDER PRACTICE

1. Details in the photo might lead students to infer that Eckford and other members of the "Little Rock Nine" faced resistance from whites, verbal abuse, racial hatred, potential physical harm, and so on.

2. Inferences may focus on the impact Little Rock had on the attitudes of some whites and on the pride that the event instilled in many African Americans.

Chapter 21, Section 1
RETEACHING ACTIVITY

1. In *Plessy* v. *Ferguson*, the Supreme Court ruled that the notion of "separate but equal" was constitutional, while the *Brown* decision essentially reversed that ruling.

2. He placed the Arkansas National Guard under federal control and ordered troops into Little Rock to protect African-American students trying to desegregate the school.

3. It began after Rosa Parks was arrested for refusing to leave her seat on a bus so a white man didn't have to sit next to her; in 1956, the Supreme Court outlawed bus segregation.

4. It was the first piece of civil rights legislation since Reconstruction; it gave the attorney general greater power over school desegregation and gave the federal government jurisdiction over violations of African-American voting rights.

5. Non-violent resistance and civil disobedience

6. The demonstrators sat passively as whites beat and humiliated them.

Chapter 21, Section 2
RETEACHING ACTIVITY

freedom rides—led to the banning of segregation in all interstate travel facilities; march on Birmingham—convinced President Kennedy that only a new civil rights act could end racial violence; Civil Rights Act of 1964—prohibited discrimination based on race, religion, national origin, or gender and outlawed segregation of public accommodations; 24th Amendment—outlawed the poll tax, a

measure used to keep African Americans from voting; march on Selma—prompted President Johnson to push for swift passage of a voting rights act; Voting Rights Act of 1965—eliminated literacy tests as a requirement for voting and helped to greatly increase the number of African American voters

Chapter 21, Section 3
RETEACHING ACTIVITY

1. c   2. a

3. a   4. d

5. b   6. b

Chapter 21, Section 1
GEOGRAPHY APPLICATION

Responses may vary on the inferential questions.

1. Delaware, Maryland, West Virginia, Missouri, Texas, and Arkansas

2. Louisiana, Georgia, South Carolina, Alabama, and Mississippi

3. Generally, the earlier a state began to desegregate its schools, the more integrated its schools were in 1964; Arkansas.

4. Oklahoma, Missouri, Maryland, and Delaware

5. Texas, Tennessee, Virginia, Louisiana, North Carolina, South Carolina, Florida, Arkansas, Mississippi, Alabama, and Georgia

6. Arkansas, Mississippi, Alabama, Georgia, and South Carolina; these were states in which there had been great numbers of slaves before the Civil War, so in them the separation of the races had the weight of history, and the desegregation of public schools was therefore unpopular.

Chapter 21, Section 1
PRIMARY SOURCE

Crisis in Little Rock

Students may say that the hostile reaction was caused by racial prejudice; the fact that the South had a long tradition of segregation and some whites resisted change; and the fact that white Southerners did not want the federal government to tell them what to do. They may also point out that the

National Guard troops reacted in a hostile manner because Governor Faubus had ordered them to keep the black students out of Central High School.

Chapter 21, Section 2
PRIMARY SOURCE

Civil Rights Song

1. Informally assess students' discussion. You may want to have students share the lyrics to other protest songs such as those from Prohibition or from the Vietnam era.

2. Have the class listen to recordings of civil rights protest songs. Then discuss similarities and differences. Informally assess students' participation in the discussion.

Chapter 21, Section 2
PRIMARY SOURCE

"I Have a Dream"

1. Students may say he means that he believes it will give social equality and equal opportunity to people, regardless of race or religion.

2. Students may say that he speaks of injustice and oppression, of "vicious racists," and of a governor who denies and nullifies federal laws mandating equality.

3. Students may point out that African Americans have gained some legal, social, and economic equality but that injustice and racial discrimination still exist.

Chapter 21, Section 2
PRIMARY SOURCE

Political Poster

1. The images of a group of united African Americans and a broken chain; the slogans "We Shall Overcome" and "Register—Vote"

2. Students will likely feel that the image of a broken chain and the slogan "We Shall Overcome" are most persuasive.

3. Students' images and slogans will vary but should convey the idea that voting is a key to freedom.

Chapter 21, Section 2
LITERATURE SELECTION

And All Our Wounds Forgiven

1. Informally assess the clarity and historical accuracy of students' reports. You may want to have them create a photo gallery of civil rights leaders.

2. Through their research, students will find that Patrice Lumumba was the appointed premier of the newly independent African country of Zaire and was assassinated in February 1961 after being deposed; Chet Huntley and David Brinkley were a news team on NBC's "Huntley-Brinkley Report."

Chapter 21, Section 1
AMERICAN LIVES

Rosa Parks

Possible responses:

1. Parks is called the "mother of the civil rights movement" because her action in Montgomery launched the first successful mass protest of segregation laws.

2. Because Parks's character was beyond criticism, it was easy for African Americans to rally in her support and difficult for racists to find fault with her.

3. Parks showed that one person, however ordinary, can make a difference.

Chapter 21, Section 2
AMERICAN LIVES

A. *Philip Randolph*

Possible responses:

1. Randolph was referring to the Jim Crow laws that segregated the South. At the time, the Army was segregated as well.

2. The New Deal passed laws that gave greater power to unions. Those gains helped Randolph get Pullman to recognize the Brotherhood.

3. Support: Randolph was right to cancel the 1941 march because he had won some concessions from President Roosevelt. Oppose: Randolph should have held the march to show Roosevelt that he needed to do more.

Chapter 22, Section 1
GUIDED READING

A. Possible answers:

1. Vietnam's independence
2. That Vietnam was a nation
3. Vowed to fight from North Vietnam to liberate the South
4. France
5. Economic aid (for military purposes)
6. To prevent another Asian country from becoming Communist
7. Countries verging on communism
8. Surrendered; pulled out of Vietnam
9. Divided it along the 17th parallel
10. Ngo Dinh Diem, with U.S. support; feared that Ho Chi Minh and the Communists would win
11. Broad military powers in Vietnam
12. Bombed the North

B. Answers will vary widely depending upon the specifics noted.

Chapter 22, Section 2
GUIDED READING

Possible answers:

1. Johnson: Made decision to escalate
   McNamara: Advised Johnson on escalation
   Rusk: Advised Johnson on escalation
   Westmoreland: Requested troops
   Congress: Approved of Johnson's policies
   Public: Approved of Johnson's policies
2. Americans: Superior weaponry
3. Vietcong: Knowledge of terrain; ability to blend in with civilians; willingness to pay any price for victory
4. U.S.: Bombings; war of attrition; preventing Vietcong support by South Vietnam's rural population; the use of napalm and Agent Orange; search-and-destroy missions
5. Vietcong: Hit-and-run ambushes; booby traps and land mines; surprise attacks; guerrilla warfare
6. Economy: The costs of the war led to an increase in inflation and taxes, as well as to a reduction in funding

for Great Society programs

TV: Brought the war into U.S. living rooms; contradicted the Johnson administration's optimistim

Hearings: Contributed to the average American's growing ambivalence about the war

Chapter 22, Section 3
GUIDED READING

Possible answers:

1. Found doctors to give medical deferments; looked for lenient draft boards; joined the National Guard or Coast Guard; enrolled in college

2. Nearly 80 percent of U.S. soldiers came from lower economic levels; a common way to get a deferment was by enrolling in college, which generally required having money.

3. New Left organizations; Students for a Democratic Society (SDS); the Free Speech Movement (FSM); college students; the young

4. Johnson's revoking college deferments for those not in good academic standing; the belief that the war did not concern the U.S.; the belief that the war was draining U.S. strength; the belief that the war was immoral

5. Held antiwar demonstrations in public areas; publicly burned draft cards; fled to Canada and Sweden; marched on Washington

6. Supported U.S. involvement

7. Felt that Johnson should escalate the war more quickly

Chapter 22, Section 4
GUIDED READING

A. Possible answers:

1. Causes: The Vietnam War; the Vietcong's push to capture cities in South Vietnam

   Effects: A military defeat for the Vietcong; a dramatic fall in the popularity of Johnson and the war; Johnson's decisions to change his Vietnam policy and not to seek reelection

2. Causes: The Tet Offensive; the unpopularity of his Vietnam policy; the growing popularity of Eugene McCarthy's antiwar message

Effects: Robert Kennedy's decision to run for president; Johnson's decision not to run for reelection

3. Causes: Racism; hatred; intolerance; an atmosphere of violence

   Effects: Feelings of anger and despair among his followers; violent riots in more than 100 U.S. cities

4. Causes: Hatred; an atmosphere of violence in the country

   Effects: Feelings of despair and hopelessness among his followers

5. Causes: Disagreements among Democrats over Vietnam; the presence of 10,000 demonstrators with differing goals; Daley's handling of the situation; the poor judgment and brutality of the Chicago police

   Effects: The negative image of the Democratic party; a Republican presidential victory

6. Causes: The negative image of the Democratic party; the desire for the peace, law, and order that Nixon had promised; the entry of Wallace into the race

B. Answers will vary widely depending upon the specifics noted.

Chapter 22, Section 5
GUIDED READING

A. Possible answers:

1. Vietnamization: To replace U.S. troops with South Vietnamese troops; to establish "peace with honor"

2. My Lai: 200 innocent Vietnamese murdered by U.S. soldiers

3. Invasion: To remove Vietnamese and Vietcong supply centers from Cambodia

4. Strike: To protest the invasion of Cambodia

5. Tonkin: To protest Nixon's bombing and invasion of Cambodia without notifying Congress; to gain greater Congressional control over U.S. policy in Vietnam

6. Bombings: To force a negotiated peace settlement

7. Surrender: North Vietnam's full-scale invasion of South Vietnam and the capture of Saigon; no U.S. troops there to prevent the North's

victory

8. Veterans: Americans very torn and bitter about the war

9. Civil war: The U.S. invasion of Cambodia

10. War Powers: To curb the president's war-making powers

11. Draft: It was extremely unpopular.

12. Faith: The Pentagon Papers, which revealed that the Johnson administration was lying about the war; the My Lai massacre; the government's response to campus turmoil at Kent State; the Nixon administration's lying; the Watergate scandal

B. Answers will vary widely depending upon the specifics noted.

Chapter 22
BUILDING VOCABULARY

A.

1. c   2. a   3. b
4. c   5. a

B.

1. War Powers Act
2. William Westmoreland
3. domino theory
4. New Left
5. Pentagon Papers

C. Answers will vary depending on the specifics noted.

Chapter 22, Section 2
SKILLBUILDER PRACTICE

1. fact   2. opinion
3. opinion   4. fact
5. fact   6. opinion
7. opinion   8. fact
9. fact   10. opinion

Chapter 22, Section 1
RETEACHING ACTIVITY

A. Truman—pumped nearly $1 billion into France's effort to defeat the Vietminh; Eisenhower—continued supplying aid to the French, supported Ngo Dinh Diem's refusal to hold nationwide election and sup-

plied military aid and training to his government; Kennedy—increased aid to Diem's regime and sent thousands of military advisers to help train South Vietnamese troops; supported coup to replace Diem; Johnson—convinced Congress to pass Tonkin Gulf Resolution giving the president broad military powers; unleashed bombing campaign; sent in U.S. combat troops

B.

1. The Vietminh wanted a free and independent Vietnam, while France sought to regain power in Vietnam, which had been a French colony.

2. Vietnam was temporarily divided along the 17th parallel into North and South and a future election would be held to unify the country.

3. A declaration passed by Congress that gave the president broad military powers in Vietnam

Chapter 22, Section 2
RETEACHING ACTIVITY

1. A majority of Americans supported Johnson's decision; they believed he was following an established policy of confronting communism.

2. Hit-and-run ambush tactics, lack of a traditional front, numerous tunnel networks, land mines and booby traps

3. The use of napalm and Agent Orange, which destroyed much of the countryside, and search-and-destroy missions, which leveled villages and left millions of refugees

4. The frustrations of guerrilla warfare, the brutal jungle conditions, the failure to gain against the enemy, and the corruption

5. It hurt the Great Society because Johnson had to redirect millions of dollars in funding from his domestic programs to the war effort.

6. Television aired daily footage of hard-fought battles. U.S. casualties seemed to contradict the Johnson administration's contention that the war was proceeding well.

Chapter 22, Section 3
RETEACHING ACTIVITY

A.

1. f	2. g	3. e
4. h	5. d	6. a
7. c	8. b	

B.

1. F—During the years of anti-war protest, about 10,000 Americans fled the country in order to escape military service.

2. T

3. T

4. F—Martin Luther King Jr. criticized the war and argued that African Americans were dying for a country that still considered them second-class citizens.

5. F—Many of the men who fought in Vietnam were either lower-class whites or minorities.

Chapter 22, Section 4
RETEACHING ACTIVITY

A.

1. 3	2. 4
3. 1	4. 6
5. 2	6. 5

B.

1. Walter Conkrite

2. Israel

3. Columbia University

4. law and order

5. Yippies

Chapter 22, Section 5
RETEACHING ACTIVITY

1. b	2. d
3. c	4. b
5. a	6. b

Chapter 22, Section 4
GEOGRAPHY APPLICATION

Responses may vary on the inferential questions.

1. The trail began in southern North Vietnam, and extended southward through eastern Laos and Cambodia, with a number of branches extending into various parts of South Vietnam.

2. The trail provided a way for North Vietnam to send troops and supplies to support its Vietcong allies fighting in South Vietnam.

3. more than 400 miles (or 650 kilometers)

4. South Vietnamese troops, with U.S. air support, invaded Laos in an attempt to cut the flow of troops and supplies from North Vietnam into South Vietnam.

5. A successful invasion of Laos would have cut the Ho Chi Minh Trail and may have been able to prevent the Vietcong from receiving enough North Vietnamese troops and supplies to continue the war. Thus, a successful invasion could have affected the outcome of the war.

6. The length of the Ho Chi Minh Trail allowed the North Vietnamese to mount simultaneous attacks over the entire length of South Vietnam. The attacks in the far south probably could not have been made without the support provided by the Ho Chi Minh Trail.

Chapter 22, Section 5
OUTLINE MAP

1. the Mekong River

2. China shares North Vietnam's northern border and could easily have supplied troops to the fighting on behalf of North Vietnam after the U.S. entered the war.

3. Hanoi; Saigon

4. less than 50 miles

5. North Vietnam would have been able to attack South Vietnam only through the bottleneck of DMZ land or by launching attacks by sea—both options that South Vietnam and the United States could have better defended against.

6. nearly 500 miles

7. Cambodia, Thailand, and possibly even Malaysia, Indonesia, and the Philippines

Chapter 22, Section 2
PRIMARY SOURCE

Letter from a Soldier in Vietnam

1. It is a distinguished-looking, thornless plant with soft red flowers.

2. Students may say that the plant reminds him of his Aunt Fannie and also of Vietnam. They may explain that he compares the beautiful plant, which grows in the midst of an inhospitable jungle, to a beautiful thought, gesture, or person that unexpectedly arises in the midst of war-torn Vietnam.

3. Students may say that Kempner is able to see beauty amidst ruins. They may infer that his humanity, dignity, and intelligence help him cope with the inhumanity of war.

Chapter 22, Section 3
PRIMARY SOURCE

Protest Buttons

1. Informally assess each group's discussion. Make sure that students adequately explain their choices of the most effective protest buttons.

2. Informally assess students' buttons and encourage them to display or wear them in the classroom.

Chapter 22, Section 3
PRIMARY SOURCE

The New Left

1. Students may point out any of the following: the opportunity to make history, to feel useful, to take part in and to have control over what happened, to gain a sense of purpose, to be part of a community

2. The New Left was cliquish. Members often felt pulled away from old friends, yet were unable to become part of the "inner circle."

3. Some students may say that in contrast to the conformity of the 1950s, the New Left of the 1960s was exciting and meaningful. Others may point out that the New Left attracted young people who were opposed to the Vietnam War and wanted to work for social change. A few students may feel that the New Left attracted young people because it

was the "in" thing

Chapter 22, Section 4
PRIMARY SOURCE

Lyndon B. Johnson on Vietnam and Reelection

1. He offered to stop bombing North Vietnam as long as serious peace talks between the United States and North Vietnam began.

2. Johnson chose not to run because he did not want to get involved with partisan politics and he felt the need to devote his full attention to the presidency while the country was at war in Vietnam.

3. Some students may suggest that antiwar activists would have greeted Johnson's speech enthusiastically because he took a decisive step toward peace and because he paved the way for an antiwar presidential candidate like Eugene McCarthy. Others may suggest that antiwar activists would have been disappointed because Johnson merely announced an end to escalation, not an end to the war.

Chapter 22, Section 5
LITERATURE SELECTION

In Country

Informally assess students' research. Encourage them to include information on the mementos left by visitors at the base of the walls as well as these additions to the memorial: the Frederick Hart sculpture *Three Servicemen* that was dedicated on November 1, 1984, and the Glenna Goodacre Vietnam Women's Memorial that was dedicated on November 11, 1993.

Chapter 22, Section 2
AMERICAN LIVES

Robert McNamara

Possible responses:

1. McNamara was a good manager, as shown by his success at Ford Motor Company, in reforming the Defense Department, and in changing the direction of the World Bank.

2. McNamara came to think that the war was a mistake because it could

not be won.

3. Agree: McNamara had a responsibility to express his doubts in order to save people's lives by helping end the war sooner. Disagree: McNamara had a duty to protect his boss—the president—and his former colleagues from second guessing.

Chapter 22, Section 4
AMERICAN LIVES

John Lewis

Possible responses:

1. Lewis's commitment to nonviolence was tested when he was beaten, especially in Montgomery during the freedom ride and at the Edmund Pettus Bridge.

2. In his quote, Lewis is saying that violence may bring quick and easy success at first but it dishonors a person and can only lead to bad consequences.

3. Lewis's opposition to the use of force in 1991 is the same as his principled stand for nonviolence and against the Vietnam War in the 1960s.

Chapter 23, Section 1
GUIDED READING

Possible answers:

1. Actions: César Chávez formed two unions, including the United Farm Workers Organizing Committee; he went on a three-week fast and launched a nationwide boycott of grapes.

   Laws: none

2. Actions: Various groups fought for classes taught in Spanish, smaller classes, more Chicano teachers and administrators, programs to reduce the dropout rate, programs in Latino studies; students held strikes.

   Laws: Bilingual Education Act

3. Actions: The Mexican American Political Association (MAPA) sponsored candidates, registered and educated voters, and lobbied for legislation; La Raza Unida sponsored a number of winning candidates; Reies Tijerina founded the Alianza Federal de Mercedes to help reclaim U.S. land taken from

Mexican landholders in the 1800s.

   Laws: none

4. Actions: A group of 61 Native American organizations drafted the Declaration of Indian Purpose, which advocated self-determination, an end to the termination program, and policies that would create economic opportunities on reservations.

   Laws: The Indian Education Act; the Indian Self-Determination and Education Assistance Act

5. Actions: Various groups used militant actions to confront the government; the Indians of All Tribes seized and occupied Alcatraz; the American Indian Movement (AIM), led by Russell Means, seized and occupied the Bureau of Indian Affairs building in Washington, D.C., and the town of Wounded Knee; various groups took their land claims to federal court.

   Laws: Alaska Native Lands Claim Settlement Act

Chapter 23, Section 2
GUIDED READING

A. Possible answers:

1. Workplace: Widespread wage and job discrimination awakened many women to their inferior social status.

2. Activism: Discrimination that women faced within the civil rights and antiwar movements awakened them to their unequal treatment.

3. Consciousness-raising: Helped women to discover that their personal experiences were part of a larger pattern of discrimination

4. Feminism: Provided a theory for the movement

5. Friedan: Encouraged women to organize and take action

6. Act: Gave women legal tools to fight discrimination

7. NOW: Actively pursued the movement's social and political goals

8. *Ms:* Informed women about the women's movement

9. Congress: Banned gender discrimination in educational and other activities supported by federal funds; expanded the EEOC's enforcement powers; gave working

parents tax breaks for child-care expenses

10. Court: In *Roe* v. *Wade*, recognized women's right to have an abortion during the first three months of pregnancy

B. Possible answers:

1. Who: Conservative political and religious groups; antifeminists; Phyllis Schafly; the Stop-ERA campaigns

2. Why: Antifeminism; fears that it would lead to the drafting of women, the end of laws protecting homemakers, and same-sex marriages; fears about its impact on families; fear that it would end a husband's responsibility to provide for his family

Chapter 23, Section 3
GUIDED READING

1. Members: Idealistic or disillusioned young people; white, middle-class youths; hippies; people experimenting with drugs; followers of Eastern religions

2. Beliefs: It had grown hollow, materialistic, cold, and cruel; it was best to "tune in, turn on, drop out."

3. Goals: An idyllic setting of peace, love, and harmony—the Age of Aquarius; greater self-awareness and inner peace; living together in communes and renouncing private property

4. Centers: San Francisco's Haight-Ashbury

5. Activities: Listening to and playing rock 'n' roll music; wearing outrageous clothing; using drugs; living in communes; attending concerts; casualness and individuality—"do your own thing"

6. Violence: urban communes became dangerous; the deaths of Janis Joplin and Jimi Hendrix from drug overdoses

7. Art and fashion: A rebellious style of pop art and a more consumer-oriented mass art

8. Music: The widespread popularity and growth of rock; the popularity of the Beatles; the Woodstock music festival

9. Mainstream America: A more casual

approach to sexual and social behavior; the sexual revolution; a conservative backlash; Nixon's election

Chapter 23
BUILDING VOCABULARY

A.

1. d   2. e
3. b   4. f
5. a   6. c

B.

1. b   2. a
3. c   4. a

C. Answers will vary depending on the specifics noted.

Chapter 23, Section 3
SKILLBUILDER PRACTICE

1920s: jazz; short, straight dresses; short, close hair styles; bright make-up

Both: movements against the established society of the times; freer relationships between men and women; some people thought they were immoral; not all young people participated in the movement; representations of changes taking place in U.S.

1960s: rock 'n' roll; worn jeans or long, flowing dresses; soft, loose, long hair; no make-up

Chapter 23, Section 1
RETEACHING ACTIVITY

1. c   2. a
3. b   4. c
5. d   6. b

Chapter 23, Section 2
RETEACHING ACTIVITY

A. Gains—EEOC declares sex-segregated job ads illegal and mandates that employers could no longer refuse to hire women for traditionally male jobs; Gloria Steinem forms *Ms.* Magazine to cater to feminist issues; Congress passes ban on gender discrimination in education; Congress gives tax break to working parents for child-care expenses; *Roe* v. *Wade* upholds woman's right to have an

abortion; more women become doctors and lawyers; number of women in Congress increases; Setbacks—Equal Rights Amendment meets with defeat; New Right emerges to battle many feminist issues; women continue to hit a "glass-ceiling" in the workplace

B.

1. That many women felt unfulfilled and were dissatisfied with their status in society; it helped to galvanize women across the country and fuel the women's movement

2. Many women in these movements faced discrimination and sexism from their male counterparts, which opened their eyes to their inferior status and prompted many to begin challenging the system.

3. They feared that it would lead to many things that women would not want, such as the drafting of women and the end of a husband's responsibility to provide for his family.

Chapter 23, Section 3
RETEACHING ACTIVITY

1. that Americans had grown too materialistic and hollow

2. to drop out of mainstream society and create idyllic communities of peace, love, and harmony

3. Rock 'n' roll music, outrageous clothing, sexual license, illegal drugs, long hair, and adherence to alternative religions

4. The counterculture communities grew dangerous and violent, and many hippies realized that they could not earn a living outside of mainstream society.

5. Pop art became popular among many Americans, while rock 'n' roll eventually became a hit with mainstream America.

6. They believed that it promoted decadent values and abandoned rational thought in favor of uninhibited self-expression.

CURRICULUM

Chapter 23, Section 2
GEOGRAPHY APPLICATION

Responses may vary on the inferential questions.

1. to prohibit discrimination solely based on gender

2. 35

3. Within a year of Congress's sending the amendment to the states, 30 states had voted for ratification, and only 8 more states were needed over the next six years.

4. Idaho, South Dakota, Nebraska, Kentucky, and Tennessee; none of them

5. the Deep South; the Southwest and the southern part of the Midwest

6. The ERA was the first amendment ever to reach the end of its seven-year time limit without being ratified, and Congress for the first time extended the length of time allowed for the ratification of an amendment.

7. it would have been approved; it would have been approved

Chapter 23, Section 1
PRIMARY SOURCE

The Farm Worker Movement

1. Responses will vary but may include the following reasons: because a farmworker told the NFWA about abuses in the rose industry, because rose grafters did highly skilled work but were paid significantly less than they were promised, and because Mount Arbor was the largest rose growing company.

2. They had a pledge ceremony, checked people's homes to make sure they were not going to work, and physically prevented several workers from leaving their driveway.

3. Some students may say that boycotts and strikes like the one Chávez describes were powerful tools in gaining some economic justice for farmworkers. Others may say that farmworkers still are among the lowest paid and hardest working in the country and that they have yet to attain social and economic equality.

Chapter 23, Section 1

PRIMARY SOURCE

United Farm Workers Poster

1. Carnegie Hall in New York City

2. Alan King; Peter, Paul & Mary

3. Students may say that the poster conveys a sense of cultural pride, a message of hope, and the promise of a better future.

Chapter 23, Section 2
PRIMARY SOURCE

The Feminine Mystique

Through their research, students will find that more women today are single, have attended college, and are employed. They will also find that women today still earn less than men do for the same work.

Chapter 23, Section 3
PRIMARY SOURCE

Popular Song

1. Informally assess students' participation in the class discussion. You may wish to have students write their responses as liner notes.

2. Before students begin, you may want to provide them with examples of 1960s album covers for ideas. Informally assess students' designs.

3. You may want to have one or two students act as DJs to introduce and play the music. Then have students explain their choices, comparing each piece with "Woodstock."

Chapter 23, Section 1
LITERATURE SELECTION

Los Vendidos

1. Informally assess students' discussions. Guide them to discuss these stereotypes: Honest Sancho, the secretary, the farmworker, and the Mexican American. Have them analyze whether the use of satire in this excerpt is an effective weapon against stereotyping.

2. Informally assess students' sketches. You may want some students to perform their sketches for the class.

3. Informally assess students' playbills

on the basis of creativity and on how effectively they reflect the social purpose and spirit of *actos*.

Chapter 23, Section 1
AMERICAN LIVES

César Chávez

Possible responses:

1. Chávez means that the person using nonviolence sometimes has to face punishment without fighting back.

2. Migrant workers were unable to organize because growers hired strikebreakers.

3. Chávez was so poor that he had to beg for food. He also went on a hunger strike at one point. His weekly salary was only $5.

Chapter 23, Section 2
AMERICAN LIVES

Betty Friedan

Possible responses:

1. By refusing to publish articles dealing with women's careers, the magazines reinforced the idea that women should be concerned only about their home lives.

2. King helped energize people to join the civil rights movement. Friedan helped energize women to join the feminist movement.

3. Some feminists thought that in *The Second Stage* Friedan was emphasizing family too much.

Weeks-Townsend Memorial Library
Union College
Barbourville, KY 40906